Cooperative Learning &
Mathematics
High School Activities

by Dina Kushnir

Kagan

Kagan Publishing
P.O. Box 72008
San Clemente, CA 92673-2008
1 (800) 933-2667
Fax: (949) 545-6301
www.KaganOnline.com

ISBN: 978-1-879097–57–5

Table of Contents

Chart of Structures III
Pre-Algebra Overview IV
Algebra 1 Overview. VI
Geometry Overview VIII
Algebra 2 & Trigonometry Overview X
Pre-Calculus Overview XII
Foreword. 1
Introduction 5

Structures for Mathematics

1 Mix-N-Match

Pre-Algebra
- Activities 15
- Blackline Masters 23

Algebra 1
- Activities 27
- Blackline Masters 33

Geometry
- Activities 37
- Blackline Masters 41

Algebra 2
- Activities 45
- Blackline Masters 55

Trigonometry
- Activities 45
- Blackline Masters 59

Pre-Calculus
- Activities 65
- Blackline Masters 69

2 Line-Ups

Pre-Algebra
- Activities 77
- Blackline Masters 81

Algebra 1
- Activities 87
- Blackline Masters 91

Geometry
- Activities 97
- Blackline Masters 99

Algebra 2
- Activities 103

Trigonometry
- Activities 103
- Blackline Masters 111

Pre-Calculus
- Activities 115
- Blackline Masters 119

3 Inside-Outside Circle

Pre-Algebra
- Activities 127
- Blackline Masters 135

Algebra 1
- Activities 143
- Blackline Masters 147

Geometry
- Activities 157
- Blackline Masters 161

Algebra 2
- Activities 169
- Blackline Masters 177

Trigonometry
- Activities 169
- Blackline Masters 177

Pre-Calculus
- Activities 193
- Blackline Masters 197

Table of Contents cont.

4 RallyCoach

Pre-Algebra
- Activities 209
- Blackline Masters 215

Algebra 1
- Activities 219
- Blackline Masters 225

Geometry
- Activities 229
- Blackline Masters 233

Algebra 2
- Activities 237
- Blackline Masters 245

Trigonometry
- Activities 237
- Blackline Masters 255

Pre-Calculus
- Activities 259
- Blackline Masters 263

5 RoundTable

Pre-Algebra
- Activities 271
- Blackline Masters 275

Algebra 1
- Activities 281
- Blackline Masters 287

Geometry
- Activities 299
- Blackline Masters 303

Algebra 2
- Activities 309
- Blackline Masters 313

Trigonometry
- Activities 309
- Blackline Masters 319

Pre-Calculus
- Activities 325
- Blackline Masters 331

6 Mix-Pair-RallyCoach

Pre-Algebra
- Activities 341
- Blackline Masters 345

Algebra 1
- Activities 351
- Blackline Masters 355

Geometry
- Activities 361
- Blackline Masters 363

Algebra 2
- Activities 369
- Blackline Masters 375

Trigonometry
- Activities 369
- Blackline Masters 375

Pre-Calculus
- Activities 381
- Blackline Masters 387

7 More Mathematics Structures

- Fan-N-Pick 396
- Find Someone Who 397
  - Activity 398
- Mix-Freeze-Group 399
- Numbered Heads Together 400
- Pairs Check 401
- Showdown 402
- Telephone 403
  - Activity 404
- Timed Pair Share 405

Chart of Structures

Structures	Pre-Algebra Activities	Pre-Algebra Blacklines	Algebra 1 Activities	Algebra 1 Blacklines	Geometry Activities	Geometry Blacklines	Algebra 2/Trigonometry Activities	Algebra 2/Trigonometry Blacklines	Pre-Calculus Activities	Pre-Calculus Blacklines
Mix-N-Match	15	23	27	33	37	41	45	55	65	69
Line-Ups	77	81	87	91	97	99	103	111	115	119
Inside-Outside Circle	127	135	143	147	157	161	169	177	193	197
RallyCoach	209	215	219	225	229	233	237	245	259	263
RoundTable	271	275	281	287	299	303	309	313	325	331
Mix-Pair-RallyCoach	341	345	351	355	361	363	369	375	381	387

Kagan Publishing • 1 (800) 933-2667
www.KaganOnline.com

Cooperative Learning Activities for High School Mathematics
Dina Kushnir

Pre-Algebra
Activities &

Mix-N-Match
Activities

1. Operations on Fractions 15
2. Order of Operations 15
3. Exponential Form 16
4. Scientific Notation. 16
5. Area, Perimeter, and Volume. 16
6. Greatest Common
   Factor or Least Common Multiple 17
7. Passage of Time 17
8. Place Value 17
9. More Place Value. 18
10. Properties of Arithmetic 18
11. Equivalent Rational Expressions. 19
12. Problem Solving With Percent 19
13. Solving One-Step Equations 19
14. Inequalities in One Variable 20
15. Unit Price 20
16. Solving Proportions. 21
17. Geometry Definitions 21
18. The Counting Principle. 22
19. Statistics. 22

Blackline

1. Properties of Arithmetic 23

Line-Ups
Activities

1. Comparing the Values of Fractions,
   Decimals, and Percents 77
2. Area, Perimeter, and Volume. 77
3. Statistics. 78
4. Order of Operations 78
5. Rounding. 78
6. Greatest Common
   Factor or Least Common Multiple 79
7. Operations on Fractions 79
8. Problem Solving with Proportions 79
9. Angle Measurement. 80
10. The Counting Principle. 80

Blackline

1. Order of Operations. 81

Inside-Outside Circle
Activities

1. Area and Perimeter 127
2. Place Value 128
3. Rounding. 128
4. Greatest Common Factor and
   Least Common Multiple 128
5. Order of Operations 129
6. Properties of Arithmetic 129
7. Operations on Integers 129
8. Comparing Fractions 130
9. Converting Fractions, Decimals, and Percents 130
10. Interpreting Data and Graphs 130
11. Simplifying Algebraic Expressions 131
12. Operations on Monomials. 131
13. Inequality Graphs 131
14. Percents. 132
15. Converting Units. 132
16. Symmetry 132
17. Simple One-Step Equations. 133

Blackline

1. Percent Problems. 135

Blacklines

RallyCoach
Activities

1. Factors of a Number 209
2. Common Factors. 210
3. One-Step Equations. 210
4. Operations on Integers 211
5. Equivalent Decimals, Fractions, and Percents 211
6. Interpreting Graphs. 212
7. Problem Solving with Decimals, Fractions, and Percents 212
8. Measurement, Surface Area, and Volume . . 213
9. Order of Operations 213
10. Properties of Numbers 213

Blackline

1. Problem Solving with percents, Decimals, and Fractions 215

RoundTable
Activities

1. Operations on Fractions 271
2. Operations on Decimals 271
3. Operations on Integers 272
4. Statistics. 272
5. Probability. 273
6. Rounding. 273
7. Interpreting Graphs and Other Data Displays . 274

Blackline

1. Probability 275

Mix-Pair-RallyCoach
Activities

1. Operations on Fractions 341
2. Operations on Integers 341
3. Operations on Decimals 342
4. Passage of Time. 342
5. Percent of a Number 342
6. Percent Decrease (and Percent Increase) . . 343
7. Surface Area and Volume of Prisms 343
8. Greatest Common Factor and Least Common Multiple 344

Blackline

1. Surface Area and Volume. 345

Algebra 1

Activities &

Mix-N-Match

Activities

1. Writing Algebraic Expressions 27
2. Evaluating Algebraic Expressions 27
3. Simplifying Algebraic Expressions 28
4. Operations on Monomials 28
5. Operations on Polynomials 29
6. Linear Equations 29
7. Factoring 30
8. Reducing Rational Expressions 30
9. Adding Fractions with
   Monomial Denominators 31
10. Slope-Intercept Form of a Line 31
11. Evaluating Square Roots 32
12. Operations on Radicals 32

Blackline

1. Reducing Rational Expressions 33

Line-Ups

Activities

1. Evaluating Algebraic Expression 87
2. Linear Equations in on Variable 87
3. Quadratic Equations 88
4. Linear Equations in Two Variables 88
5. Algebra Word Problems 88
6. Solving Systems of Equations 89

Blackline

1. Evaluating Algebraic Expressions 91

Inside-Outside Circle

Activities

1. Writing Algebraic Expressions 143
2. Operations on Polynomials 143
3. Factoring 144
4. Slope of a Line 144
5. Irrational Numbers 144
6. Simplifying Radicals 145
7. Completing the Square 145

Blackline

1. Factoring 2nd Degree Polynomials (or Multiplying Polynomials and Monomials) 147

Blacklines

ALGEBRA 1

RallyCoach

Activities

1. Writing Algebraic Expressions 220
2. Evaluating Algebraic Expressions 220
3. Solving Multi-Step Linear Equations 221
4. Writing Multi-Step Equations 221
5. Operations on Radicals 222
6. Graphing Linear Functions 222
7. Algebra Word Problems in One Variable . . . 223
8. Writing, Evaluating, Transforming Formulas . 224
9. The Real Number System 224

Blackline

1. Writing, Evaluating, and Transforming Formulas. 225

RoundTable

Activities

1. Algebra Word Problems in on Variable 281
2. Algebra Word Problems in
   Two Variables (Algebraic Solution) 282
3. Algebra Word Problems in
   Two Variables (Graphic Solution) 282
4. Operations on Monomials 283
5. Operations on Polynomials 283
6. Operations on Rational Expressions
   (Also Known as Algebraic Fractions 284
7. Writing the Equation of a Line 284
8. Operations on Radicals 285
9. Solving Quadratic Equations 285

Blacklines

1. Solving Algebra Word Problems with One Variable 287
2. Solving Algebra Word Problems with a System of Equations 293

Mix-Pair-RallyCoach

Activities

1. Operations on Polynomials 351
2. Operations on Monomials 351
3. Writing and Solving Linear Equations 352
4. Solving Systems of Linear Equations 352
5. Irrational Numbers 353

Blackline

1. Writing and Solving Linear Equations 355

Geometry

A c t i v i t i e s &

Mix-N-Match
Activities

1. Geometry Definitions 37
2. Angle Measures 37
3. Segment Lengths 38
4. Circle Theorems 38

5. Coordinate Geometry 39
6. Transformational Geometry 39
7. Compositions of Transformations 40

Blackline

1. Transformational Geometry 41

Line-Ups
Activities

1. Interior and Exterior Angles of a Polygon . . 97
2. Lengths of Segments 97

3. Circle Theorems 98
4. Coordinate Geometry 98

Blackline

1. Angle Measures 99

Inside-Outside Circle
Activities

1. Geometry Definitions 157
2. Beginning Geometry Proofs 157
3. Truth Value of a Given Statement 158
4. Finding Angle Measures 158
5. Congruent Triangles 158

6. Properties of Quadrilaterals 159
7. Special Right Triangles (30-60-90 Triangles and 45-45-90 Triangles) 159
8. Transformational Geometry

Blackline

1. Beginning Geometry Proofs (Using Geometry Definitions) 161

B l a c k l i n e s

RallyCoach

Activities

1. Constructions 230
2. Geometry Proofs 230
3. Geometry Problem Solving 231
4. Properties of Quadrilaterals. 232
5. Corresponding Parts of Congruent Triangles . 232

Blackline

1. Constructions 233

RoundTable

Activities

1. Constructions 299
2. Geometry Proofs 300
3. Circle Problems 300
4. Geometry Definitions 301
5. Geometry Definitions (with Diagram) 301
6. Quadrilaterals 302
7. Similar Right Triangles 302

Blackline

1. Special Right Triangles 303

Mix-Pair-RallyCoach

Activities

1. Coordinate Geometry 361
2. Transformational Geometry. 361
3. More Transformations 362

Blackline

1. Coordinate Geometry 363

Algebra 2 & Trigonometry
Activities

Mix-N-Match
Activities

1. Equations of Lines. 45
2. Absolute Value Equations 46
3. Evaluating Functions 46
4. Inverses of Functions 47
5. Domain and Range of a Function 47
6. Graphing Parabolas. 48
7. Fractional and Negative Exponents 48
8. Simplifying Rational Expressions
   with Negative Exponents 48
9. Direct, Inverse, and Joint Variation. 49
10. Powers of "i" 49

11. Operations on Imaginary and
    Complex Numbers 50
12. Equation of a Circle. 50
13. Evaluating Logarithms 51
14. Solving Log Equations. 51
15. Degree Measure and Radian Measure 51
16. Trig Function Values of Special Angles. 52
17. Graphs of the Sine and Cosine Curves 52
18. Trig Functions and Reference Angles 52
19. Inverse Trig Functions 53
20. Right Triangle Trigonometry. 53

Blacklines

1. Negative Exponents 55
2. Graphs of Trigonometric Functions 59

Line-Ups
Activities

1. Absolute Value Equations/Radical Equations . 103
2. Evaluating Functions 103
3. Compositions of Functions. 104
4. Inverse of a Function 104
5. Writing the Equation of a Line 104
6. Writing Quadratic Equations 105
7. Direct Variation. 105
8. Undefined Fractions 105
9. Repeating Decimals. 106
10. Quadratic Formula 106
11. Parabolas. 106

12. Logarithms 107
13. Exponential and Logarithmic Equations. . . 107
14. Finding Angle Measures
    Using Trigonometric Functions 107
15. Finding Segment Lengths
    Using Right Triangle Trigonometry. 108
16. Reference Angles. 108
17. Understanding Radian Measure 108
18. Radian and Degree Measure 109
19. Angle Sum and Angle Difference Formulas . 109
20. Solving Trigonometric Equations 109

Blackline

1. Finding Angle Measure Using All Six Trig Functions. 111

Inside-Outside Circle
Activities

1. Right Triangle Trigonometry. 169
2. Evaluating Absolute Value Expressions . . . 169
3. Identifying Functions 170
4. Domain and Range of a Function. 170
5. Rational Expressions. 170
6. Imaginary Numbers (Powers of "i") 171

7. Fractional and Negative Exponents 171
8. Operations on Complex Numbers 171
9. Graphs of Quadratic Functions (Parabolas) 172
10. Equations of Circles 172
11. Evaluating Logarithms 172
12. Laws of Logarithms. 173

Blacklines

Inside-Outside Circle Cont.

Activities

13. Trig Functions in All Four Quadrants 173
14. Trig Function Values for Special Angles ... 173
15. Permutations and Combinations
    (Word Problems) 174
16. Graphs of Trig Functions 174
17. Angle Sum and Difference Formulas 174
18. Inverse Trig Functions 175

Blacklines

1. Trigometric Values of Special Angles (0, 30, 45, 60, 90, 180, 270, 360) 177
2. Evaluating Logarithms 185

RallyCoach

Activities

1. Coordinate Geometry Proofs............ 238
2. Laws of Sines and Cosines, Area of a Triangle . 238
3. Right Triangle Trigonometry............ 239
4. Function Graphs (Compositions and Inverses) . 239
5. Linear Equations in Two Variables 240
6. Solving Systems of Equations by Graphing. 241
7. Graphing Conic Sections............... 241
8. Graphing Linear Equations in three Variables. 242
9. Trigonometric Graphs................. 242
10. Measures of Central Tendency 243
11. Solving Quadratic Equations........... 243

Blacklines

1. Solving Systems of Equations by Graphing 245
2. Statistics 251
3. Right Triangle Trigonometry......................... 255

RoundTable

Activities

1. Coordinate Geometry 309
2. Compositions and Inverses of Functions .. 310
3. Trigonometric Functions on the
   Non-Unit Circle..................... 310
4. Transformations on the Coordinate Plane.. 311
5. Complex Numbers 312
6. Trigonometric Graphs................. 312

Blacklines

1. Compositions of Functions and Inverses of Functions 313
2. Trigonometric Functions on the Non-Unit Circle 319

Mix-Pair-RallyCoach

Activities

1. Absolute Value Equations and Inequalities. 369
2. Compositions of Functions 369
3. Writing the Equation of a Line 370
4. Angle Sum and Angle Difference Formulas. 370
5. Graphing System of Inequalities........ 371
6. Graphing Trig Functions............... 371
7. Operations on Complex Numbers 372
8. Advanced Probability Combinations...... 372
9. Binomial Expansion 373
10. Equation of a Circle.................. 373

Blackline

1. Angle Sum and Difference Formulas......................... 375

Pre-Calculus
Activities &

Mix-N-Match
Activities

1. Evaluating Determinants 65
2. Arithmetic and Geometric Progressions 65
3. Polynomial Function Graphs 66
4. Converting Equations Form Polar to Rectangular Form (and Vice Versa) 66
5. Laws of Logarithms 67
6. Factor Theorem and Remainder Theorem . . 67
7. Binomial Expansion 68
8. Venn Diagrams 68

Blackline

1. Polynomial Functions and Their Graphs 69

Line-Ups
Activities

1. Determinants 115
2. Arithmetic and Geometric Progressions . . . 115
3. Sum of an Arithmetic or Geometric Series . 116
4. Remainder Theorem 116
5. Matrices 116
6. Distance From a Point to a Line 117
7. Angle of Inclination 117
8. Summation 117

Blackline

1. Arithmetic and Geometric Progressions 119

Inside-Outside Circle
Activities

1. Determinants 193
2. Series and Sequences 193
3. Identifying Conic Sections 194
4. Special Factoring Techniques 194
5. Writing Functions 194
6. Rational Functions 195
7. Using the Scientific Calculator 195

Blackline

1. Identifying Conic Sections 197

Blacklines

PRE-CALCULUS

RallyCoach
Activities

1. Graphing Interval Functions 260
2. Geometric Progressions 260
3. Linear Programming 261
4. Polar Coordinates and Demoiver s Theorem . 262

Blackline

1. Linear Programming 263

RoundTable
Activities

1. Solving Systems of Equations
   Using Determinants. 325
2. Domain and Range of a Function 326
3. Coordinate Geometry 326
4. Interval Functions. 327
5. Graphing Rational Functions 327
6. Discriminant and the Roots of a
   Quadratic Equation 328
7. Interpreting Function Graphs. 328
8. Transformations of Functions 329
9. Compositions of Functions. 329
10. Writing Functions 330

Blackline

1. Graphing Rational Functions 331

Mix-Pair-RallyCoach
Activities

1. Determinants. 381
2. Arithmetic Series and Sequences 381
3. Geometric Series 382
4. Parabolas. 382
5. Rational Function Graphs. 383
6. Distance from a Point to a Line. 383
7. Linear Functions. 384
8. Solving Exponential Equations Using Logs 384
9. Vectors. 385

Blackline

1. Parabolas. 387

Foreword

Are you a high school mathematics teacher looking for ways to add ZING to your classroom? Are you looking for alternatives to the traditional lecture approach? Have you tried putting students into work groups and wondered why it failed miserably? Have you had the good intention of trying cooperative strategies but thought that it seemed too complicated and labor intensive? If you answered "yes" to any of these questions, then this book is for you!

The purpose of this book is to provide high school mathematics teachers with cooperative learning lessons they can *easily* and *effectively* implement into their teaching repertoire. The lessons and activities in this booklet are based on techniques developed by Spencer Kagan. These strategies will be explained and developed where appropriate throughout the book. One of the great aspects of the Kagan model is that you do not need to overhaul everything you are already doing in order to implement cooperative strategies. The lessons in this book can be used within the context of what most teachers are already doing, but they can significantly increase student involvement, achievement, and accountability.

There is a vast difference between "group work" and "cooperative learning." Many teachers (myself included) have put students into groups, given them a task to complete, and told them to work together on that task. Ideally, one would hope that the stronger students would help the weaker students to learn the concepts necessary to complete the task. One would also hope that everyone would be actively engaged in the learning activity, and that each student would pull his or her weight in the completion of the task at hand. Unfortunately, these ideals are not usually achieved. Instead, one often sees some students doing all the work while others "sit out," due to either lack of motivation or lack of ability. There is often no incentive for the weaker students to learn the concepts at hand because the stronger students can simply give them the answers. There is no incentive for the unmotivated students to get involved because the more concerned group members will take care of their share of the work load. In either situation, the "group work" situation has become a breeding ground for resentment, between the students themselves, and between students and teachers. To top it off, no real learning is likely to take place, even though the worksheet is filled in or the math problem gets solved.

Kagan's model of cooperative learning is called the "structural approach," and it is designed to help teachers overcome the obstacles described above. A structure is simply the way you organize an activity. The structure you use indicates the way in which students will interact in regards to the content. There are over 100 different structures in the Kagan model, each designed to help teachers achieve different objectives. Each structure incorporates four key principles, commonly referred to as PIES. They are:

1. **Positive Interdependence:** A gain for one is a gain for another. Students need each other to complete the given task.

2. **Individual Accountability:** Individual public performance is required of all students. There is no hiding in the shadows. Structures insure that everyone is required to do something.

3. **Equal participation:** Structures in this book help insure that no one dominates the group, and that no one is able to sit back and let others carry the load.

4. **Simultaneous interaction:** Each activity attempts to get as many students overtly active at once. The activities aim to get *at least* 25% of the students in the class doing mathematics at any given time.

As stated earlier, there are over 100 structures in the Kagan model. The structure you choose depends on your objectives. Structures can be used for team-building, class-building, teaching thinking skills, teaching communication skills, sharing information, checking for understanding, mastering content, and much more. In this book, I have chosen to focus on six structures which I believe are most useful for the teaching of mathematics. These structures will help students master content and develop higher level thinking skills. Each chapter is devoted to a single "structure" and includes a detailed description of how to most effectively implement that structure. Following the description is a list of topics for which that structure would be an effective teaching tool. The list is divided into activities for Pre-Algebra, Algebra 1, Geometry, Algebra 2 and Trigonometry, and PreCalculus. Examples of activities for each of the aforementioned courses are included at the end of each chapter. The activities are designed so that teachers can simply reproduce the pages in this book and get down to the business of teaching.

The last chapter in the book contains a summary of eight other structures which lend themselves to the teaching of mathematics

The activities included in this book can only be successful if students have the will and motivation to participate. Using grades as a motivator is strongly discouraged. When grades are used, students become more focused on the grade than on learning, or helping others learn. Students may worry about how their performance might affect other people's grades, or how their grade might be adversely affected by others. A much better way to motivate students and encourage their will to participate is by doing Classbuilding and/or Teambuilding exercises.

A Classbuilding exercise is any activity during which students learn more about the other people in the class and/or develop an identity as a class. A Teambuilding exercise allows students to focus on getting to know the people in their cooperative team. These exercises help students to get to know each other better, and help create a positive climate. Through Teambuilding and Classbuilding, students learn to value individual differences and appreciate each other's talents. A mutual

support system can then evolve as students participate in the learning activities. Many of the structures featured in this book can be easily modified and used for Classbuilding or Teambuilding. These exercises don't have to take a lot of class time! Often, one or two minutes is enough for students to do, for example, a Round Table on who their favorite movie actor is. If such exercises are done a few times per week, the improved classroom climate will be well worth the time spent on them.

The activities in this book are only a small sampling of how cooperative techniques can be implemented into the high school mathematics classroom. My hope is that the ideas presented here will act as a springboard for teachers, who can then develop their own activities and adjust them to fit their particular content. With a little practice and some willingness to experiment, using cooperative techniques will add new life to your classroom! Whenever I try a new cooperative activity, students invariably tell me how much more they enjoy learning mathematics. May you find the activities and strategies presented in this book to be useful, effective, and fun! Good luck!

Dina Kushnir
Mathematics Teacher
Fayetteville–Manlius High School

Introduction

Why Use Cooperative Learning?

Why is it important to use cooperative learning? You are, after all, a busy math teacher. You barely have enough planning time to make your worksheets and tests, let alone develop a whole mess of new "cooperative learning activities." And you have a curriculum to get through, for crying out loud! There's no time for silly "feel good" games and activities! Besides, doesn't "cooperative learning" mean that a few kids do all the work while others just leech off of their efforts and hard work? Won't the high achievers be held back by the slower students? What are we really gaining by using these strategies anyway?

There are many misconceptions about a) what cooperative learning is and b) how to effectively use cooperative strategies in the classroom. There are teachers who agree that cooperative learning is beneficial in theory, but that it takes a tremendous amount of extra planning and materials to put it into practice. I would like to briefly address some of these misconceptions and share with you some of the benefits of cooperative learning.

Let's first address why cooperative learning is important. We are certainly in the midst of the "information age," an era in which analyzing and communicating information plays a vital role in the economy and the world at large. Unfortunately, you cannot communicate information alone. Interaction is required. In many workplaces today, employees work in teams to generate data, solve problems, and develop strategies for success. Our students need to be prepared for this type of environment if they are to compete in the job market. Not only do they need to learn the social and communication skills necessary to work with others, they also need to develop higher level thinking skills. It can no longer be presumed that social and communication skills are taught at home. Today, many of our young people face the challenges of single parent homes or homes where both parents work full time. Many families relocate, often more than once, tearing students away from the familiar stabilizing influences they once too relied on. With less contact and guidance from concerned adults, students are spending more time than ever in front of the television. Their values and self images are being shaped by poor role models and the advertising spin doctors from Madison Avenue. They are continually exposed to violent, racist, or overtly sexual content. Schools need to do something to teach students how to get along together, tolerate differences, feel good about themselves, and help one another. Cooperative learning is one solution to America's socialization problem. Numerous studies show that students involved in cooperative learning develop a wider variety of social skills,

are better able to work with others in solving problems, and are more willing to help and praise others.

No other educational innovation has been more intensely researched than cooperative learning. In addition to improved social skills, cooperative learning strategies produce many other positive outcomes. Studies show that students involved in cooperative learning activities enjoy improved relations between races. These students had a greater tendency to choose friends from an ethnic group other than their own. Students in cooperative classrooms also demonstrate greater self-esteem and tend to like class more. Cooperative activities also tend to lower students' anxiety level, since students have more peer support and opportunities to receive praise.

"But what about scholastic achievement?" you ask. Research proves that cooperative learning produces higher academic achievement than individualistic or traditional teacher-centered methods. This is true at all levels and across all subject areas. Minority groups and low achievers tend to experience the greatest gains, but this has no negative impact on the higher achieving students. In fact, high achievers perform just as well, if not better, in a cooperative environment than in a traditional one. Cooperative learning activities produce greater achievement results because they create more opportunities for peer tutoring than do traditional classroom methods. A well-structured cooperative lesson also forces students to spend more time on task and to have more interaction in regards to the academic content. In a cooperative classroom, the teacher actually spends less time lecturing and is therefore able to give more individual attention to the neediest students.

Most of the teachers I have talked to say that their worst discipline problem is students talking or engaging in off-task behaviors. Cooperative strategies work with students' natural tendencies rather than against them. Students need to communicate, and to stifle that natural tendency is virtually impossible. Yet traditional classroom techniques require students to sit quietly for large blocks of time and absorb everything the teacher says. As teachers, we get frustrated when this doesn't happen, yet the traditional classroom structure predisposes us to failure! Cooperative activities channel the students' need to socialize in a positive direction, rather than attempt to stifle it all together. If you do not give students a chance to interact with their peers, they will take the opportunity anyway, usually in the form of "disobedience." The cooperative structures presented in this book build in "individual accountability," so there is little opportunity for students to engage in off-task behavior.

Is It Difficult To Incorporate Cooperative Learning Into My Teaching Repertoire?

In my opinion, one of the best features of the structural approach is that you do not have to scrap everything you are already doing in order to use cooperative learning. Think of the structures as though they were tools in a tool box. A carpenter doesn't use a hammer for every carpentry job. He selects the tool that is most appropriate for the task at hand. Think of a lesson as a carpentry project for which you will use many different tools. In a cooperative learning lesson, the structures are your tools. There will be times when direct teaching or lecturing is the most appropriate tool to use, but you will also reach into your "structure tool box" to achieve various objectives. Cooperative activities can be used to

help students practice newly learned material and achieve mastery. They can also be used to go over homework or generate discussion on the best way to study for a test. A lesson might consist of a RoundRobin, some direct teaching, a Timed Pair Share, some more direct teaching, and finally an Inside-Outside Circle activity. Depending on your objectives, the structures can be used in many different ways. In my classroom, I use a blend of direct teaching and cooperative structures. Not only is this blend fitting to my learning objectives, it also helps kids learn to adapt to a variety of different social situations.

You can try cooperative learning in small doses at first in order to get comfortable with a classroom set up in teams. Select a structure or two that you feel confident using and play around with them in the classroom. The structures themselves are content free, so once you learn a structure you can use it in an infinite number of ways! Some of the easiest structures to get started with are presented in this book, along with many ideas on how to use them in the mathematics classroom. As you practice using the various structures, you will be able to determine which ones work best for you and you will be able to refine them to meet your particular needs. One thing is certain, however: you will see kids get excited and involved! The achievement gains of your students will encourage you to try more structures more often.

Is It Very Time Consuming To Use Cooperative Learning?

I have found that planning a cooperative learning lesson does not take any more time to plan than a traditional lecture-style lesson. I simply spend my time differently.

Previously, I spent a lot of time planning out what notes I would write on the board for students to copy down in their notebooks. Of course I still do some of that, which is entirely appropriate, but I have cut down considerably. The students did not benefit much from watching me do 5 sample problems on a single topic. They learn much more by watching two or three examples, followed by a cooperative activity which gives them a chance to practice. What time I used to spend writing notes I now spend making flashcards, for example, or writing a RoundTable record sheet.

One of the misconceptions I had about cooperative learning was that I would have to write a million worksheets and keep track of all kinds of fancy score cards. Fortunately, the Kagan model does not require any more paperwork than traditional teaching methods. It will require more thought, however, as you familiarize yourself with the structures and determine the best way to use them in your classroom. In the end, you will find that your efforts have paid off in terms of students' academic achievement, development of social skills, reduction in discipline problems, and a positive classroom climate.

Cooperative activities do not necessarily take up a lot of classroom time. A Timed Pair Share might take one minute, while a Rally Table might take 5 or 10 minutes. You can design cooperative activities to be as short or long as you need them to be. A Mix-n-Match activity can take anywhere from 3 minutes to 15 minutes depending on how many new partners you allow the students to match up with. The structures presented in this book are flexible enough to use under any time constraint.

How Do I Manage a Cooperative Classroom?

When I first began using cooperative techniques in my classroom, I admit I was scared!! I was afraid things would get out of control and I would never be able to get back the attention of the students. All my life I had been taught in a traditional classroom, so there was no role model for me to follow. To my knowledge, no one else in my school was using cooperative strategies, so I felt I was experimenting on my own. I was really competent when it came to managing 30 kids sitting in rows, but managing teams was another story!

By and large, many of your classroom management problems will decrease as a result of switching to cooperative learning. Cooperative strategies are more in line with students' basic need to interact with each other, so you will spend less time trying to keep kids quiet and in their seats. Students are encouraged to talk and move around, so what was once a "discipline problem" can actually become an asset to students' learning!

However, managing a cooperative classroom does involve a different set of skills than a traditional classroom. Most of the students in your class may have no experience in working with teams, so remember that they may be uncomfortable adjusting, too!! Some concerns that you will need to address are appropriate noise level, active listening techniques, managing materials, and seating arrangements. When students are in groups and involved in a learning activity, there is a natural tendency for the classroom to get too noisy. As the teacher, you may want to reduce the noise level, or perhaps you need the undivided attention of the class so you can give further instructions. For years I would yell, "Can I have your attention please?" or "Ladies and gentlemen , I need you to be quiet now." I would get little or no response, which irritated me, and I was only adding more noise to an already loud classroom! Instead, the Kagan model suggests the use of a "quiet signal." When a teacher needs students to be quiet, (s)he raises his/her hand. The students in turn raise their hands to signal others and give the teacher their attention. There are many variations of quiet signals. You can develop your own! Another way to keep noise level down is to assign one person on each team the role of "Quiet Captain." It is this person's job to alert teammates if they are too loud.

As you introduce a structure to students, they will need to be very clear on the directions. It is recommended that directions be given both verbally and visually to accommodate different learning styles. As you say the directions, you can simultaneously write them on a chalkboard or overhead. Most of the structures involve several steps. Give directions only one step at a time, and make sure everyone understands each individual step before moving on to the next one. You can check for understanding in a variety of ways. Students may respond in unison to questions posed by the teacher, or they may do a Thumbs Up/ Thumbs Down response to statements given by the teacher. When finished, leave the steps posted so students can refer back to them if necessary. It is also beneficial to model the steps of a structure with the students. You may choose a student or team and role play an activity in front of the class. This is also a great way to model the social skills you want them to develop, such as praising, active listening, respecting other's opinions, and offering help.

For a more thorough overview of management techniques, refer to chapter 8 of Dr. Spencer Kagan's book *Kagan Cooperative Learning*. In this chapter, you will read about these and many more powerful management techniques.

How Do I Get Started? How Do I Use This Book?

As explained in the Foreword, there is a big difference between "cooperative learning" and "group work." In order for an activity to be considered cooperative learning, it must meet four criteria, commonly referred to as "PIES"...

Positive Interdependence—a gain for one student is a gain for other students; students need each other to complete the given task.

Individual Accountability—individual public performance is required.

Equal Participation—no one "sits out," and no one can dominate the activity

Simultaneous Interaction—getting as many students overtly active as possible at any given time.

The good news is that you do not need to translate these abstract concepts into classroom practice because they are already inherent in the structures. PIES is already built in to every activity presented in this book.

Each chapter in this book is devoted to a single structure. First, a description of the structure is given, along with some helpful hints on how to implement that structure in the classroom. While structures can be used to achieve many different objectives, the activities in this book are designed to help students master mathematical content. Following the description of the structure, you will find extensive lists of the ways that structure can be used to teach high school mathematics. The lists are categorized according to the various levels of mathematics taught in most high schools: Pre-Algebra, Algebra 1, Geometry, Algebra 2 and Trigonometry, and Pre-Calculus. At the end of each list, you will find blackline masters for one or more of the activities mentioned, usually one for each course level. You are free to reproduce these and use them in your classroom.

You can do an awful lot of cooperative learning just by reproducing the blackline masters given in this book, but my hope is that this book will be a launching pad for your own ideas. A structure can never be exhausted, because it is content-free. A structure only becomes an activity after you add in the content. The first thing I suggest that you do is read through the descriptions of all the

structures presented in this book. It won't take long, since the structures are uncomplicated and easy to understand. Then, think about what topics you are teaching in the next few days and ask yourself which structure seems fitting to your topic and objectives. You might find that topic is already listed several times in the book under different structures. (A topical index is included at the end of the book.) If it's not, you yourself might come up with your own new idea! Remember, a structure is only a "tool" and it's up to you to decide how, when, why, and for how long to use it. The art of using cooperative learning is knowing which structure to use when, and this art is developed through practice.

So go ahead...turn the page and start reading! As you read the descriptions of the structures, you will be surprised how many times you say to yourself, "Hey! I can really use this!"

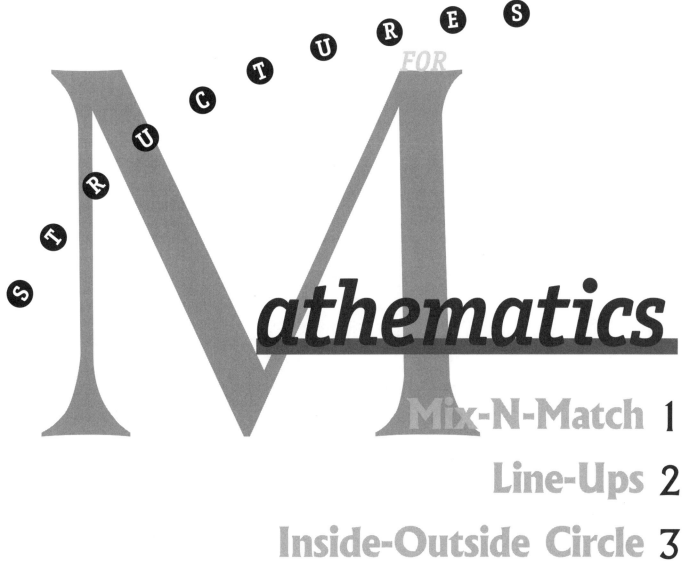

STRUCTURES FOR Mathematics

Mix-N-Match 1

Line-Ups 2

Inside-Outside Circle 3

RallyCoach 4

RoundTable 5

Mix-Pair-RallyCoach 6

Kagan Publishing • 1 (800) 933-2667
www.KaganOnline.com

Cooperative Learning Activities for High School Mathematics
Dina Kushnir

Mix-N-Match

Steps at a Glance

1. With a card in their hand, each student mixes around the room. Each finds a partner, and quizzes him or her by asking a question relating to their card.

2. Partner answers. Praise or coaching is given.

3. Switch roles: The other partner asks then praises or coaches.

4. Partners trade cards.

5. Partners split up and repeat Steps 1 through 4 a number of times. Teacher calls "Freeze!"

6. Students freeze, hide their cards, and think of their match.

7. Students move to the center of the room, find their match, and quickly move away from the center of the room with their new partner.

   Optional: Teacher may post a class graph to record the time it takes for students to find their matching partners. Students try to beat their class record.

In this structure, each student is given a card with some type of problem or information on it. Each student should be certain as to the correct answer to his or her problem before beginning the "Mix-N-Match." You may want to give students some time in their teams to ascertain the solutions to their problems or teachers can hand out the cards in matched pairs, so students are already sitting with a "match." Once this is done, students are to "mix" (that is, mingle about the room) and find the person with a card that "matches" theirs. For example, if each card has an equation on it, students would have to find the person whose solution is the same as theirs. As students pair up, they should move to the outside perimeter of the classroom and stand together as a pair. Once everyone has found their match, students can confer with another nearby pair to double check that they do indeed make a match. When everyone is satisfactorily paired up, the teacher can then collect the cards and redistribute them

MIX-N-MATCH

for another round (if desired). The possibilities for this structure in the math classroom are endless!

One possible pitfall to this structure is that an unmotivated or struggling student may simply stand around and wait for his match to find him, thus managing to get through the activity without really doing any work. (Remember the "E" in "PIES": Equal participation is the goal!) One way to avoid this is to have the students do several "quiz and swaps" before finding their match. Students would mingle and form random pairs and quiz each other regarding the content on their cards. If both partners get the correct answers, they swap cards, and then find another random partner. If anyone gets an incorrect answer, their partner should re-teach him before swapping cards. After several swaps, the teacher

would yell, "Freeze! Find your match!" At this point students would purposely seek out the person whose card is equivalent to theirs.

On the next several pages, you will find a list of ideas for incorporating the Mix-N-Match structure into your teaching repertoire.

Following this list are several sets of Mix-N-Match cards that are ready to use. Simply reproduce one set of cards for the class, pass them out, and let students search for their matches. If you have an odd number of students, have two students walk around with one card, or the teacher can participate in the activity. Each set in this book contains 30 cards (15 matching pairs). You may have to remove a matching pair or two to account for smaller class sizes. Just make sure that whatever cards you remove are indeed a "match."

Mix-N-Match Contents

PRE-ALGEBRA

- Activities 15
- Blackline Masters 23

ALGEBRA 1

- Activities 27
- Blackline Masters 33

GEOMETRY

- Activities 37
- Blackline Masters 41

ALGEBRA 2

- Activities 45
- Blackline Masters 55

TRIGONOMETRY

- Activities 45
- Blackline Masters 59

PRE-CALCULUS

- Activities 65
- Blackline Masters 69

Management Tips

1 This structure works best with short answer questions or problems that only require one or two steps.

2 If a set of Mix-N-Match cards is divided into "A cards" and "B cards," use a different color card stock for each.

3 Students put a hand up as they mix to find a partner; hands go down when a partner is found.

4 Students move to the perimeter of the room when they find their match.

5 Allow students to carry slates or clipboards with paper to do scratchwork.

6 Pass out cards in matched pairs to partners on a team. If students know they are sitting next to a match before mixing, it prevents wrong answers from circulating through the class.

Social Skills

1 Greeting someone

2 Giving and accepting praise

3 Giving and accepting constructive criticism

4 Coaching others (rather than giving the answer)

5 Departing gambits

6 Appropriate noise level

Mix-N-Match
Pre-Algebra

1. OPERATIONS ON FRACTIONS

Students are to evaluate a problem involving addition, subtraction, multiplication, or division of fractions. Students are to match up with the person whose problem yields the same answer. A similar Mix-N-Match can be done for *Operations on Decimals* or *Operations on Integers*. It is recommended that students be allowed to carry slates with them for this activity.

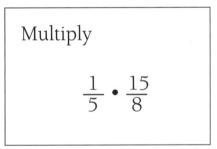

Multiply

$$\frac{1}{5} \cdot \frac{15}{8}$$

$$\frac{1}{8} + \frac{1}{4}$$

2. ORDER OF OPERATIONS

Students are to evaluate an expression involving several binary operations, which may also include parentheses. Students are to match up with the person whose problem yields the same answer. It is recommended that students be allowed to carry slates with them for this activity.

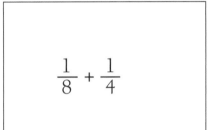

$$\frac{70 - 5 \cdot 2}{3^2 - 4}$$

$$(2 + 3)^2 - 13$$

3. EXPONENTIAL FORM

Half of the cards are **A cards** which contain a factored expression, such as **4x4x4xKxK**. The other cards are **B cards** which contain an exponential expression, such as **4^3K^2** Students are to match up so that each factored expression is paired with its equivalent exponential expression.

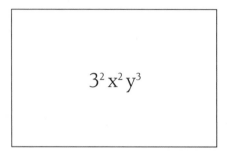

$$3 \cdot 3xxyyy \qquad\qquad 3^2x^2y^3$$

4. SCIENTIFIC NOTATION

Half of the cards are **A cards** which contain a whole number or decimal, such as **.00000034**. The other half are **B cards** which contain numbers written in scientific notation, such as **3.4×10^{-7}**. Students are to match up so that each whole number or decimal is paired with its equivalent scientific notation expression.

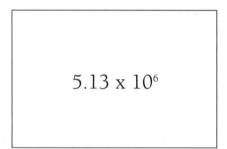

$$5{,}130{,}000 \qquad\qquad 5.13 \times 10^6$$

5. AREA, PERIMETER, AND VOLUME

Students are to find the area, perimeter or volume of a figure or solid drawn on their card. Students are to match up with the person whose problem yields the same answer. It is recommended that students be allowed to carry slates with them for this activity.

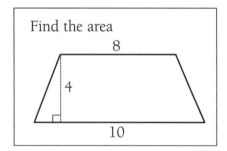

Find the area

8

4

10

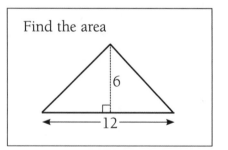

Find the area

6

12

6. GREATEST COMMON FACTOR OR LEAST COMMON MULTIPLE

Students are to find the GCF or LCM of a set of whole numbers. Students are to match up with the person whose problem yields the same answer.

State the LCM of 6 and 15

State the LCM of 2, 10 and 3

7. PASSAGE OF TIME

Students are to determine the number of hours and minutes that have elapsed between a given starting and stopping time. For example, **If it is 11:30 a.m. now, how much time will have passed by 6:20 p.m.?** Students are to match up with the person whose problem yields the same answer.

If it is 8:30 A.M. now, how much time will have passed by 12:45 P.M.?

If it is 2:40 P.M. now, how much time will have passed by 6:55 P.M.?

8. PLACE VALUE

Students are to identify a given place value of a given number. For example, **What digit is in the tenths place for the number 452.995?** Students are to match up with the person whose problem yields the same answer.

What digit is in the tenths place? 503.241

What digit is in the tens place? 725.309

Kagan Publishing • 1 (800) 933-2667
www.KaganOnline.com

Cooperative Learning Activities for High School Mathematics
Dina Kushnir

9. MORE PLACE VALUE

Half the cards are **A cards** which contain whole numbers, such as **3,671**. The other cards are **B cards** which contain the expanded versions of those whole numbers, such as **3 x 1000 + 6 x 100 + 7 x 10 + 1**. Students are to match up so that each whole number is paired with its equivalent expanded expression.

4,204.3	$4 \times 1000 + 2 \times 100 + 4 \times 1 + 3 \times \dfrac{1}{10}$

10. PROPERTIES OF ARITHMETIC

pgs. 24-26

On each student's card is a number sentence that demonstrates a property of arithmetic. For example, **3 + 6 = 6 + 3** or **5(x + y) = 5x + 5y**. Properties included in this activity may include commutative property of addition, commutative property of multiplication, associative property of addition, associative property of multiplication, distributive property, identity property of addition, identity property of multiplication, additive inverse property, multiplicative inverse property. Students are to match up with someone whose number sentence exemplifies the same property as theirs.

Name the property demonstrated $7 \times (8 \times 3) = (7 \times 8) \times 3$	Name the property demonstrated $(9 \times 2) \times 6 = 9 \times (2 \times 6)$

11. EQUIVALENT RATIONAL EXPRESSIONS

Each student's card contains either a fraction, decimal, or percent. Students are to match up with the person whose card represents the same value as theirs. For example, a card that says **3/4** could match up with a card of **75%**. It is recommended that students be allowed to carry slates with them for this activity.

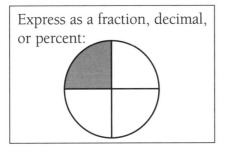

Express as a fraction, decimal, or percent:

Express...

25%

as a decimal or fraction

12. PROBLEM SOLVING WITH PERCENT

Each student's card contains a percent word problem. For example, **What is 28% of 300?** or **Find the result when 16 is increased by 75%.** Students are to match up with the person whose card represents the same value as theirs. It is recommended that students be allowed to carry calculators and/or slates with them for this activity.

What is 20% of 150?

Find the result when 24 is increased by 25%

13. SOLVING ONE-STEP EQUATIONS

Students are to solve a one-step linear equation, such as $x + 7 = 12$ or $5x = 70$. Students are to match up with the person whose equation has the same solution as theirs. A similar Mix-N-Match can be done for *Solving Two-Step Equations* or other *Multi-Step Equations*. It is recommended that students be allowed to carry slates with them for this activity.

Solve for x:

$$2x = -16$$

Solve for x:

$$x - 3 = -11$$

14. INEQUALITIES IN ONE VARIABLE

Half the cards are **A cards** which contain an inequality in algebraic form, such as $x \leq 7$. The **B cards** contain inequality graphs on a number line, such as...

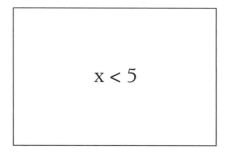

Students match up so that each algebraic inequality is paired with it's equivalent graph.

$$x < 5$$

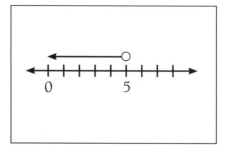

15. UNIT PRICE

Each student's card contains a price for several items. For example, **A dozen erasers costs $2.40** or **It costs $5.00 to rent 2 movies.** Students are to compute the unit price and match up with the person whose unit price is the same as theirs. It is recommended that students be allowed to carry slates and calculators for this activity.

A dozen donuts
costs $3.60.

What is the unit
price?

4 erasers cost $1.20.

What is the unit
price?

16. SOLVING PROPORTIONS

Each card contains a word problem which requires students to set up and solve a proportion. For example, **Nate types 90 words in 4 minutes. How many minutes will it take him to type 225 words?** Students are to match up with the person whose problem has the same solution as theirs. It is recommended that students be allowed to carry slates with them for this activity.

5 dictionaries weigh 30 lbs. How much to 8 dictionaries weigh?	Sue can type 72 words in 3 minutes. How many words can she type in 2 minutes?

17. GEOMETRY DEFINITIONS

Half the cards are **A cards** which state a geometry term, such as **ray** or **parallel lines**. The other cards are **B cards** which contain diagrams of these geometric terms, such as those shown below...

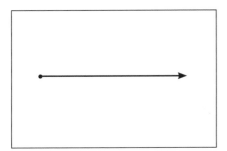
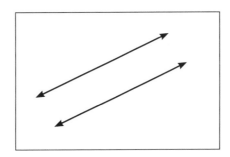

Students are to match up so that each geometric term is paired with it's appropriate diagram.

angle bisector	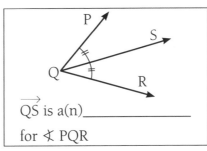

$\overrightarrow{QS}$ is a(n)_____ for ∡ PQR

18. THE COUNTING PRINCIPLE

On each student's card is a problem which requires use of the counting principle. For example, **How many ways can you fill in the answers to a true-false test with five questions if no answers are left blank?** or **How many license plates can be formed using 3 digits followed by two letters?** Students are to match up with the person whose problem has the same solution as theirs. It is recommended that students be allowed to carry slates with them for this activity.

How many ways can you fill in the answers to a true-false test with 4 questions if no answers are left blank?	How many shoe-sock combinations can you make if you own 8 pairs of socks and 2 pairs of shoes?

19. STATISTICS

Each card requires students to find either the mean, the median, or the mode of a set of data. For example, **Find the median of 56, 78, 94, and 88** or **Find the mean of 23, 34, 43, and 28**. Students are to match up with the person whose problem has the same solution as theirs. It is recommended that students be allowed to carry slates with them for this activity.

State the mode: 12, 19, 12, 13, 16	Find the mean: 15, 9, 13, 11

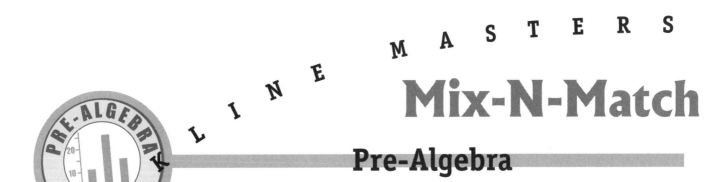

Mix-N-Match

Pre-Algebra

Properties of Arithmetic

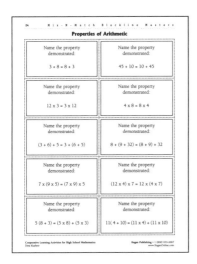

OBJECTIVES

Students will determine which property of arithmetic is demonstrated by a given equation or number sentence

MATERIALS

Mix-N-Match cards (on the following page)

DIRECTIONS

Cut out the Mix-N-Match cards and distribute them to students. Students mix (that is, mingle about the classroom) and find a partner to work with. Partners quiz each other regarding the problems on their cards. Once each partner is clear as to the correct answer, partners trade cards and mix again. Students continue to quiz and trade with partners as many times as the teacher sees fit. When the teacher yells, "Freeze! Find your match!" students purposely seek out someone whose equation demonstrates the same property as theirs and move to the perimeter of the room.

Properties of Arithmetic

Name the property
demonstrated:

$3 + 8 = 8 + 3$

Name the property
demonstrated:

$45 + 10 = 10 + 45$

Name the property
demonstrated:

$12 \times 3 = 3 \times 12$

Name the property
demonstrated:

$4 \times 8 = 8 \times 4$

Name the property
demonstrated:

$(3 + 6) + 5 = 3 + (6 + 5)$

Name the property
demonstrated:

$8 + (9 + 32) = (8 + 9) + 32$

Name the property
demonstrated:

$7 \times (9 \times 5) = (7 \times 9) \times 5$

Name the property
demonstrated:

$(12 \times 4) \times 7 = 12 \times (4 \times 7)$

Name the property
demonstrated:

$5 (8 + 3) = (5 \times 8) + (5 \times 3)$

Name the property
demonstrated:

$11 (4 + 10) = (11 \times 4) + (11 \times 10)$

Cooperative Learning Activities for High School Mathematics
Dina Kushnir

Kagan Publishing • 1 (800) 933-2667
www.KaganOnline.com

Properties of Arithmetic

Name the property
demonstrated:

$$15\,(6 - 3) = (15 \times 6) - (15 \times 3)$$

Name the property
demonstrated:

$$9\,(13 - 7) = (9 \times 13) - (9 \times 7)$$

Name the property
demonstrated:

$$34 + 0 = 34$$

Name the property
demonstrated:

$$0 + 18 = 18$$

Name the property
demonstrated:

$$53 \times 1 = 53$$

Name the property
demonstrated:

$$1 \times 22 = 22$$

Name the property
demonstrated:

$$3 + (-3) = 0$$

Name the property
demonstrated:

$$(-15) + 15 = 0$$

Name the property
demonstrated:

$$9 \times \left(\frac{1}{9}\right) = 1$$

Name the property
demonstrated:

$$\left(\frac{1}{5}\right) \times 5 = 1$$

Cooperative Learning Activities for High School Mathematics
Dina Kushnir

Properties of Arithmetic

Name the property
demonstrated:

$a + 7 = 7 + a$

Name the property
demonstrated:

$c + d = d + c$

Name the property
demonstrated:

$12 (m + n) = 12m + 12n$

Name the property
demonstrated:

$9 (y + 5) = 9y + (9 \times 5)$

Name the property
demonstrated:

$d + 0 = d$

Name the property
demonstrated:

$0 + 17 = 17$

Name the property
demonstrated:

$p \times (6 \times r) = (p \times 6) \times r$

Name the property
demonstrated:

$(10 \times 5) \times G = 10 \times (5G)$

Name the property
demonstrated:

$a\left(\dfrac{1}{a}\right) = 1$

Name the property
demonstrated:

$\left(\dfrac{1}{12}\right) \times 12 = 1$

Kagan Publishing • 1 (800) 933-2667
www.KaganOnline.com

Mix-N-Match
Algebra 1

1. WRITING ALGEBRAIC EXPRESSIONS

Half of the cards are **A cards** which contain a verbal phrase, such as **Five less than twice p** or **Half the sum of x and 6.** The other cards are **B cards** which contain algebraic expressions, such as **2p - 5** or **(x + 6)**. Students are to match up so that each verbal phrase is paired with it's algebraic equivalent.

Twice p, decreased by 5

2p - 5

2. EVALUATING ALGEBRAIC EXPRESSIONS

Each card requires students to use substitution to evaluate an algebraic expression. For example, **Evaluate $3p - 2q^2$ when p = − 4 and q = 2.** Students are to match up with the person whose problem has the same solution as theirs. It is recommended that students be allowed to carry slates with them for this activity.

Evaluate $3p^2$ - q when p = 4 and q = 10

Evaluate 2 (a + b) + 14 when a = 5 and b = 7

3. SIMPLIFYING ALGEBRAIC EXPRESSIONS

Each card requires students to simplify an algebraic expression. For example, **Simplify $2(x + y) - 4x + 5y$** or **Simplify $5p[3 - (p + 5) + 2]$**. Students are to match up with the person whose problem has the same solution as theirs. It is recommended that students be allowed to carry slates with them for this activity.

Simplify:

$3xy - x^2 + xy + 5x^2$

Simplify:

$2x(x + y) + 2x^2 + 2xy$

4. OPERATIONS ON MONOMIALS

Each card requires students to add, subtract, multiply, or divide monomials. Powers of monomials may also be included. For example, **$(3x^2)^2 = ?$** or **$4pq^3 - pq^3 = ?$** Students are to match up with the person whose problem has the same solution as theirs. It is recommended that students be allowed to carry slates with them for this activity.

Simplify:

$(2x^2)^2xy$

Simplify:

$5x^5y - x^5y$

5. OPERATIONS ON POLYNOMIALS

Each card requires students to add, subtract, multiply, or divide polynomials.
Powers of polynomials may also be included. For example,

$$(x - 5)^2 = ? \quad \text{or} \quad \frac{15x^3 + 10x^2}{5x} = ?$$

Students are to match up with the person whose problem has the same solution as
theirs. It is recommended that students be allowed to carry slates with them for this
activity.

Simplify: $(x + 3)^2$	Simplify: $\dfrac{x^3 + 6x^2 + 9x}{x}$

6. LINEAR EQUATIONS

Each card requires students to solve a linear equation. For example,
$5(x - 3) + 7x = 8x + 5$. Students are to match up with the person whose equation
has the same solution as theirs. It is recommended that students be allowed to carry
slates with them for this activity. A similar Mix-N-Match activity can be designed for
Linear Inequalities.

Solve for x: $3(x - 9) = x + 3$	Solve for x: $4x - 20 = 3x + 10 - x$

Cooperative Learning Activities for High School Mathematics
Dina Kushnir

7. FACTORING

Half the cards are **A cards** which contain a polynomial, such as
$x^2 - 25$ or $x^2 - 2x - 8$ or $5p^3 + 10p^2 + 15p$. The other cards are **B cards** which
contain factored expressions, such as $(x - 5)(x + 5)$ or $5p(p^2 + 2p + 3)$. Students
are to match up so that each polynomial is paired with its factored form. It is
recommended that students be allowed to carry slates with them for this activity.

Factor:	Express as a binomial:
$x^2 - 36$	$(x - 6)(x + 6)$

8. REDUCING RATIONAL EXPRESSIONS

Each card requires students to reduce an algebraic fraction to lowest terms by
factoring. For example,

$$\frac{y^2 - 25}{y^2 - 2y - 15} = ?$$

pgs. 34-36

Students are to match up with the person whose problem has the same solution as
theirs. It is recommended that students be allowed to carry slates with them for
this activity.

Reduce:	Reduce:
$\dfrac{x^2 - 4x + 3}{x^2 - 9}$	$\dfrac{x^2 - 2x + 1}{x^2 + 2x - 3}$

9. ADDING FRACTIONS WITH MONOMIAL DENOMINATORS

Each card requires students to add two fractions with unlike monomial denominators. For example,

$$\frac{7}{rs} + \frac{3}{2rs} = ?$$

Students are to match up with the person whose problem has the same solution as theirs. It is recommended that students be allowed to carry slates with them for this activity.

Express as a single
fraction in lowest
terms:

$$\frac{2}{p} - \frac{1}{12p}$$

Express as a single
fraction in lowest
terms:

$$\frac{1}{4p} + \frac{5}{3p}$$

10. SLOPE-INTERCEPT FORM OF A LINE

On each card is a linear equation in two variables, such as
4x − 5y = 60 or x − 3y = 9. Students are to re-write the equation in
y = mx + b form. Students then match up with the person whose line has the same slope (or y-intercept) as theirs. It is recommended that students be allowed to carry slates with them for this activity.

Find the slope
of the line
3x - 2y = 8

State the slope
of the line
4y = 6x - 16

11. EVALUATING SQUARE ROOTS

Each card requires students to evaluate an expression involving square roots. For example, $\sqrt{17}^2 - \sqrt{36}$ or $\sqrt{2}\sqrt{2} + \sqrt{64}$. Students are to match up with the person whose problem has the same solution as theirs.

Evaluate:

$$\sqrt{25} + \sqrt{19}^2$$

Evaluate:

$$\sqrt{30}\ \sqrt{30} - \sqrt{36}$$

12. OPERATIONS ON RADICALS

Each card requires students to either simplify, add, subtract, multiply, or divide radical expressions. For example, **Add $3\sqrt{2} + \sqrt{8}$** or **Simplify $3\sqrt{48}$**. Students are to match up with the person whose problem has the same solution as theirs. It is recommended that students be allowed to carry slates with them for this activity.

Find the sum in simplest form:

$$\sqrt{18} + 4\sqrt{2}$$

Divide:

$$\frac{14\sqrt{6}}{2\sqrt{3}}$$

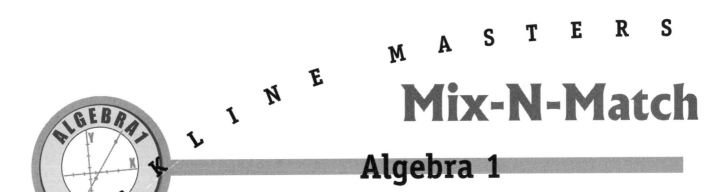

Mix-N-Match
Algebra 1

Reducing Rational Expressions

OBJECTIVES

Students will simplify rational expressions involving monomials and polynomials by factoring

MATERIALS

Mix-N-Match cards (on the following page), slates or notebooks for students to do scratchwork on

DIRECTIONS

Cut out the Mix-N-Match cards and distribute them to students. Students mix (that is, mingle about the classroom) and find a partner to work with. Partners quiz each other regarding the problems on their cards. Once each partner is clear as to the correct answer, partners trade cards and mix again. Students continue to quiz and trade with partners as many times as the teacher sees fit. When the teacher yells, "Freeze! Find your match!" students purposely seek out someone whose problem yields the same answer as theirs and move to the perimeter of the room.

Reducing Rational Expressions

Reduce: $\dfrac{x^2 - 4}{x^2 + 5x + 6}$	Reduce: $\dfrac{x^2 - 2x}{x^2 + 3x}$
Reduce: $\dfrac{x^2 + 4x + 4}{x^2 - 8x - 20}$	Reduce: $\dfrac{5x + 10}{3x - 30}$
Reduce: $\dfrac{x^2 - 4x}{2x^2 - 8x}$	Reduce: $\dfrac{2x^2 + 10x}{4x^2 + 20x}$
Reduce: $\dfrac{x^2 - 4x + 3}{x^2 + 2x - 15}$	Reduce: $\dfrac{x^2 + 3x - 4}{x^2 + 9x + 20}$
Reduce: $\dfrac{x^2 - 10x + 9}{x^2 - 4x + 3}$	Reduce: $\dfrac{x^2 - 81}{x^2 + 6x - 27}$

Reducing Rational Expressions

Reduce: $\dfrac{x^2 - 6x - 7}{3x - 21}$	Reduce: $\dfrac{x^2 - 1}{3x - 3}$
Reduce: $\dfrac{6x^2 + 30x}{3x + 15}$	Reduce: $\dfrac{2x^2 - 4x^2}{x^2 - 2x}$
Reduce: $\dfrac{2x^2 + 16x}{4x^2}$	Reduce: $\dfrac{x^2 + 3x - 40}{2x^2 - 10x}$
Reduce: $\dfrac{x^2 - 49}{x^2 - 11x + 28}$	Reduce: $\dfrac{x^2 - x - 56}{x^2 - 12x + 32}$
Reduce: $\dfrac{x^2 + 5x^2}{3x^2}$	Reduce: $\dfrac{2x^2 + 10x^2}{6x}$

Reducing Rational Expressions

Reduce:

$$\frac{x^2 - 4}{x^2 + 5x + 6}$$

Reduce:

$$\frac{x^2 - 2x}{x^2 + 3x}$$

Reduce:

$$\frac{x^2 + 4x + 4}{x^2 - 8x - 20}$$

Reduce:

$$\frac{5x + 10}{5x - 50}$$

Reduce:

$$\frac{x^2 - 4x}{2x^2 - 8x}$$

Reduce:

$$\frac{2x^2 + 10x}{4x^2 + 20x}$$

Reduce:

$$\frac{x^2 - 4x + 3}{x^2 + 2x - 15}$$

Reduce:

$$\frac{x^2 + 3x - 4}{x^2 + 9x + 20}$$

Reduce:

$$\frac{x^2 - 10x + 9}{x^2 - 4x + 3}$$

Reduce:

$$\frac{x^2 - 81}{x^2 + 6x - 27}$$

Kagan Publishing • 1 (800) 933-2667
www.KaganOnline.com

Reducing Rational Expressions

Reduce:

$$\frac{x^2 - 6x - 7}{3x - 21}$$

Reduce:

$$\frac{x^2 - 1}{3x - 3}$$

Reduce:

$$\frac{6x^2 + 30x}{3x + 15}$$

Reduce:

$$\frac{2x^3 - 4x^2}{x^2 - 2x}$$

Reduce:

$$\frac{2x^2 + 16x}{4x^2}$$

Reduce:

$$\frac{x^2 + 3x - 40}{2x^2 - 10x}$$

Reduce:

$$\frac{x^2 - 49}{x^2 - 11x + 28}$$

Reduce:

$$\frac{x^2 - x - 56}{x^2 - 12x + 32}$$

Reduce:

$$\frac{x^4 + 5x^3}{3x^2}$$

Reduce:

$$\frac{2x^3 + 10x^2}{6x}$$

Kagan Publishing • 1 (800) 933-2667
www.KaganOnline.com

Cooperative Learning Activities for High School Mathematics
Dina Kushnir

Reducing Rational Expressions

Reduce:

$$\frac{x^2 - 36}{x^2 + x - 30}$$

Reduce:

$$\frac{x^2 - 8x + 12}{x^2 - 7x + 10}$$

Reduce:

$$\frac{10x^2}{2x^3 + 12x^2}$$

Reduce:

$$\frac{5x - 30}{x^2 - 36}$$

Reduce:

$$\frac{x^2 + 8x + 7}{x^2 - 1}$$

Reduce:

$$\frac{x^2 + 4x - 21}{x^2 - 4x + 3}$$

Reduce:

$$\frac{x^2 - 7x - 8}{x^2 + 3x + 2}$$

Reduce:

$$\frac{x^2 - 6x - 16}{x^2 + 4x + 4}$$

Reduce:

$$\frac{2x^4 - 2x^3}{8x^2 - 8x}$$

Reduce:

$$\frac{x^3 + 2x^2}{4x + 8}$$

Mix-N-Match
Geometry

1. GEOMETRY DEFINITIONS

Half the cards are **A cards** which contain a geometric term, such as **supplementary angles** or **midpoint**. The other cards are **B cards** which contain the definitions of these terms. Students are to match up so that each geometric term is paired with its definition.

Define: "supplementary angles"	2 angles whose measures add to 180° are called _____

2. ANGLE MEASURES

On each students card is a geometric figure with some given information. Students are to determine the measure of the angle marked **x** or the value of the variable **x**. Some examples are shown below...

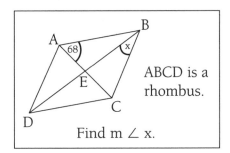

ABCD is a rhombus.

Find m ∠ x.

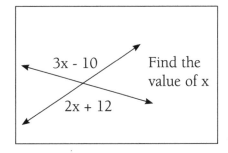

3x - 10

2x + 12

Find the value of x

Concepts incorporated into this activity may include *Properties of Quadrilaterals, Properties of Isosceles Triangles, Parallel Lines, Perpendicular Lines, Regular Polygons, Exterior Angles, Vertical Angles, Complimentary and Supplementary Angles, Similar Triangles, Angle Bisectors, Angle Sum Theorem,* and so on. Students are to match up with the person whose problem has the same solution as theirs. It is recommended that students be allowed to carry slates with them for this activity.

Kagan Publishing • 1 (800) 933-2667
www.KaganOnline.com

Cooperative Learning Activities for High School Mathematics
Dina Kushnir

3. SEGMENT LENGTHS

On each student's card is a geometric figure with some given information. Students are to determine the length of the segment marked **x** or the value of the variable **x**. Some examples are shown below...

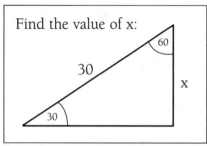

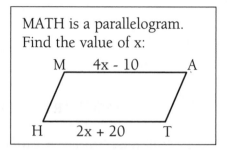

Concepts incorporated into this activity may include *Special Right Triangle Ratios, Geometric Means, Similar Triangles, Properties of Isosceles Triangles, Properties of Quadrilaterals, Pythagorean Theorem, Median of a Triangle or Trapezoid,* and so on. Students are to match up with the person whose problem has the same solution as theirs. It is recommended that students be allowed to carry slates with them for this activity.

4. CIRCLE THEOREMS

On each card is a diagram involving a circle and some given information. Students are to find the angle measure, arc measure, or segment length marked **x**. Some examples are shown below...

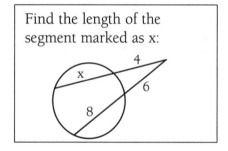

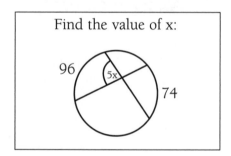

All types of circle theorems may be incorporated into this activity. Students are to match up with the person whose problem has the same solution as theirs. It is recommended that students be allowed to carry slates with them for this activity.

5. COORDINATE GEOMETRY

Each card requires students to determine the length, midpoint, or slope of a line segment whose endpoints are given. For example, **Find the length of the segment whose endpoints are (0, 5) and (–4, 2) in simplest radical form** or **Find the midpoint of the segment whose endpoints are (3, –1) and (–5, 7)**. Students are to match up with the person whose problem has the same solution as theirs. It is recommended that students be allowed to carry slates with them for this activity.

Find the distance from (1, -3) to (7, 2) In simplest radical form	Find the distance from (0, 4) to (5, -2) In simplest radical form

6. TRANSFORMATIONAL GEOMETRY

Each card requires students to determine the image of a given point under a given transformation. For example, **Find the image of (4, -1) under D_2 Find the image of (5, 3) under $R_{y\text{-axis}}$**. Students are to match up with the person whose problem has the same solution as theirs. Concepts incorporated into this activity may include *Line Reflections, Point Reflections, Rotations About the Origin, Translations,* and *Dilations*.

pgs. 42-44

Find the image of (-2, 7) under $T_{4, -1}$	Find the image of (1, 3) under a dilation of 2.

7. COMPOSITIONS OF TRANSFORMATIONS

Each card requires students to determine the image of a given point under a given composition of transformations. For example, **Find the image of (-4, 2) under the composition $R_{x\text{-axis}} \circ T_{3,1}$.** Students are to match up with the person whose problem has the same solution as theirs. Concepts incorporated into this activity may include *Line Reflections, Point Reflections, Rotations About the Origin, Translations, Glide Reflections,* and *Dilations*.

Find the image of
(4, -1) under $r_{x\text{-axis}} \circ D_2$

Find the image of
(3, 5) under $T_{3,-1} \circ r_{y=x}$

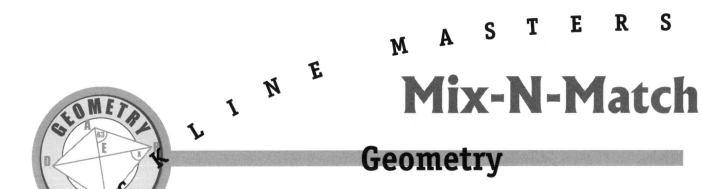

Mix-N-Match
Geometry

Transformational Geometry

OBJECTIVES

Students will determine the image of a point under a line reflection, point reflection, translation, or dilation.

MATERIALS

Mix-N-Match cards (on the following page)

DIRECTIONS

Cut out the Mix-N-Match cards and distribute them to students. Students mix (that is, mingle about the classroom) and find a partner to work with. Partners quiz each other regarding the problems on their cards. Once each partner is clear as to the correct answer, partners trade cards and mix again. Students continue to quiz and trade with partners as many times as the teacher sees fit. When the teacher yells, "Freeze! Find your match!" students purposely seek out someone whose problem yields the same answer as theirs and move to the perimeter of the room.

Transformational Geometry

$T_{4,-1} (-2, 7)$

$D_2 (1, 3)$

$r_{origin} (3, -1)$

$D_{1/2} (-6, 2)$

$r_{y-axis} (5, -2)$

$r_{origin} (5, 2)$

$r_{y=x} (-5, 2)$

$r_{x-axis} (2, 5)$

$D_{-3} (2, -1)$

$r_{y-axis} (6, 3)$

Transformational Geometry

$r_{\text{origin}}(0, -5)$

$T_{-4, 1}(4, 4)$

$r_{y = x}(-4, 5)$

$r_{y - \text{axis}}(-5, -4)$

$D_{2/3}(6, -9)$

$r_{x - \text{axis}}(4, 6)$

$T_{3, 0}(-5, 2)$

$r_{y = x}(2, -2)$

$r_{(0, 0)}(5, -2)$

$D_{1/2}(-10, 4)$

Transformational Geometry

r_{y-axis} (-1, 7)

$T_{-5,\,3}$ (6, 4)

r_{y-axis} (-4, 0)

r_{x-axis} (4, 0)

r_{origin} (4, 0)

D_2 (-2, 0)

$T_{2,\,-5}$ (1, 1)

$r_{y=x}$ (-4, 3)

$T_{2,\,2}$ (-4, 6)

D_{-1} (2, -8)

Mix-N-Match

Algebra 2 and Trigonometry

1. EQUATIONS OF LINES

Each card requires students to solve problems involving linear equations and their graphs. Some examples are given below...

> **Write the equation of a horizontal line that passes through (2, 5).**
> **Find the slope of a line that is perpendicular to y = 3x + 6.**
> **If (-1, 5) lies on the graph of 3x - ky = 8, find the value of k.**
> **State the y-intercept of the graph of 3x + 5y = 20.**

Students are to match up with the person whose problem has the same solution as theirs. It is recommended that students be allowed to carry slates with them for this activity.

State the slope of a line that would be perpendicular to

$$y = 3/2x + 7$$

State the slope of the line passing through

$$(4, 0) \text{ and } (1, 2)$$

Cooperative Learning Activities for High School Mathematics
Dina Kushnir

2. ABSOLUTE VALUE EQUATIONS

Each card requires students to solve an absolute value equation, such as $|5x - 2| = 13$. Since most of these types of problems have two answers, students may be asked to match up with the person who's larger answer is the same as theirs, or they can match up according to the sum or product of their answers. It is recommended that students be allowed to carry slates with them for this activity.

Find the smaller solution to $|3x - 1| = 13$

Find the smaller solution to $|6 - 2x| = 14$

3. EVALUATING FUNCTIONS

Each card requires students to evaluate a given function for a given variable. For example, **Find f(4) if f(x) = 3x² − 2x + 1**. Students are to match up with the person whose problem has the same solution as theirs. It is recommended that students be allowed to carry slates with them for this activity. This activity can be extended to include Compositions of Functions or Inverses of Functions. For example, **Find f(g(2)) if f(x) = 3x and g(x) = x + 7** or **Find f⁻¹ (4) if f(x) = 5x − 8**.

If $f(x) = 2x + 7$,   find $f^{-1}(19)$

If $f(x) = x^2$ and $g(x) = x - 3$,   find $g(f(-3))$

4. INVERSES OF FUNCTIONS

Half the cards are **A cards** which contain a given function f(x), such as
f(x) = 2x² or **f(x) = 10x + 6**. The other cards are **B cards** which contain a given
inverse, **f⁻¹ (x)**, such as **f⁻¹ (x) = x/2** or **f⁻¹ (x) = x - 6**. Students are to match up
so that each function, **f(x)**, is paired with its inverse, **f⁻¹(x)**.

If f(x) = 2x - 4, Find f⁻¹(x)

If f⁻¹(x)= $\dfrac{x + 4}{2}$ Find f(x)

5. DOMAIN AND RANGE OF A FUNCTION

On each student's card is a function, given as an equation, set of ordered pairs, or as
a graph. Students are to state the domain or range of the function and then match up
with the person whose answer is the same as theirs. Some examples of these types of
problems are given below...

State the domain of the function: {(3,8)(0,-1)(-2,6)}

State the domain of the function shown: 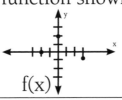

State the range of f(x): 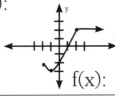

State the range of f(x): 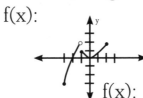

Kagan Publishing • 1 (800) 933-2667
www.KaganOnline.com

Cooperative Learning Activities for High School Mathematics
Dina Kushnir

6. GRAPHING PARABOLAS

Each card requires students to determine either the turning point, y-intercept, or axis of symmetry of an equation in the form **y = ax² + bx + c**. For example, **State the equation of the axis of symmetry for the graph of y = x² - 4x + 7** or **State the y-intercept of the graph of y = 2x² - 5**. Students are to match up with the person whose problem has the same solution as theirs.

Find the y - intercept of the graph of: $y = x^2 + 2x - 5$

State the turning point for the graph of: $y = x^2 - 5$

7. FRACTIONAL AND NEGATIVE EXPONENTS

Each card requires students to evaluate an expression involving fractional and/or negative exponents. Students are to match up with the person whose problem has the same solution as theirs.

Evaluate: $\left(\dfrac{1}{5}\right)^{-2}$

Evaluate: $(125)^{2/3}$

8. SIMPLIFYING RATIONAL EXPRESSIONS WITH NEGATIVE EXPONENTS

pgs. 56-58

Each card contains a rational expression involving monomials and negative exponents. Students are to re-write these rational expressions in simplest form using only positive exponents and match up with the person whose problem has the same solution as theirs. For example, the two cards shown below would be a "match." It is recommended that students be allowed to carry slates with them for this activity.

Simplify using only positive exponents: $\dfrac{8x^7 \, y^{-2}}{2x^2 y}$

Simplify using only positive exponents: $\dfrac{(2x)^2 \, y^{-4}}{x^{-3} y^{-1}}$

9. Direct, Inverse, and Joint Variation

Each card requires students to solve a problem involving variation. Some examples follow...

"X varies directly as Y. If X = 3 when Y = 15, find Y when X = 4.5"
"If p varies inversely as q and p = 5 when q = 12, find p when q = 15."

Students are to match up with the person whose problem has the same solution as theirs. It is recommended that students be allowed to carry slates with them for this activity.

a varies inversely as b. If a = 4 when b = 8, find a when b = 2.

a varies jointly as b and c. If a = 50 when b = 5 and c = 5, find a when b = 4 and c = 2.

10. Powers of "i"

On each student's card is a monomial or polynomial that involves powers of the imaginary unit, i., such as $5i^{10} + 3i^6 - 12i^3$ or $(2i^5)^3$. Students are to re-write the given expression in simplest **a + bi** form and match up with the person whose problem has the same answer as theirs. For example, $3i^8 - 2i^{15}$ would match up with $i^{12} + 2i^{21} + 2i^{60}$ because both are equal to **3 + 2i**. It is recommended that students be allowed to carry slates with them for this activity.

Express in a + bi form: $(3i - 4i^2)^2$

Express in a + bi form: $10i^2 + 10i^5 + 17i^8 - 14i^3$

11. OPERATIONS ON IMAGINARY AND COMPLEX NUMBERS

Each card requires students to perform an operation on complex numbers. Some examples follow...

Find the product: (2 - 3i)(4 + i).
Express in simplest a + bi form: $6i^{23} - 4i^{16} + 3i^7$
Subtract (-2 + 3i) from (11 - 4i).
Express in simplest a + bi form: $\dfrac{2}{7-3i}$

Students are to perform the indicated operation and express their answers in simplest **a + bi** form. They then match up with the person whose answer is the same as theirs.

<table>
<tr><td>

Express in a+bi
form:

$(3 + \sqrt{-16})(2 - 7i)$

</td><td>

Subtract (4 - 2i)
from:

$(38 - 15i)$

</td></tr>
</table>

12. EQUATION OF A CIRCLE

Half the cards are **A cards** which contain the equation of a circle, such as **$(x - 4)^2 + (y + 2)^2 = 17$**. The other cards are **B cards** which contain the center and radius of a circle. For example, **Center (4, - 2) and r =$\sqrt{17}$**. Students are to match up so that each circle equation is paired up with its center and radius.

<table>
<tr><td>

$(x - 4)^2 + (y + 1)^2 = 19$

</td><td>

CENTER: (4, -1)
RADIUS =$\sqrt{19}$

</td></tr>
</table>

Cooperative Learning Activities for High School Mathematics
Dina Kushnir

Kagan Publishing • 1 (800) 933-2667
www.KaganOnline.com

13. EVALUATING LOGARITHMS

Each card requires students to evaluate a log expression, such as **log.0001**
or **log₃27**. Students are to match up with the person whose log expression has
the same value as theirs.

$$\text{Log}_3\left(\frac{1}{9}\right)$$

$$\text{Log}\,(.01)$$

14. SOLVING LOG EQUATIONS

Each card requires students to find the value of x in an equation involving logarithms.
For example, $\log_3(2x + 1) = 4$ or $\log (x - 3) = 2$. Students are to match up with
the person whose problem has the same solution as theirs. It is recommended that
students be allowed to carry slates with them for this activity.

$$\text{Log}_2(x + 5) = 3$$

$$\text{Log}_5 25 = x - 1$$

15. DEGREE MEASURE AND RADIAN MEASURE

Half the cards are **A cards** which contain the degree measure of an angle, such as
210° or **75°**. The other cards are **B cards** which contain the radian measure of an
angle, such as $\frac{5\pi}{9}$ or $\frac{3\pi}{2}$. Students are to pair up so that each degree measure is paired
up with its equivalent radian measure.

$$150°$$

$$\frac{5\pi}{6}$$

16. Trig Function Values of Special Angles

On each card is written a trigonometric function of a special angle, such as **tan 45, sin 210** or **cos 300**. Students are to evaluate these trig functions in simplest radical/fractional form and match up with the person whose expression has the same value as theirs. For example, **sin 210** would match up with **cos 300** because both are equal to **-1/2**.

> Find the value of
> sin 135
> in simplest
> fractional/radical form

> Find the value of
> cos $\frac{7\pi}{4}$
> in simplest
> fractional/radical form

17. Graphs of the Sine and Cosine Curves

pgs. 61-64

Half the cards are **A cards** which contain an equation in the form **y = asin(bx)** or **y = acos(bx)**. The other cards are **B cards** which contain the graphs of these functions. Students are to match up so that each equation is paired with its graph.

> Sketch the graph of
> y = 2 sin 1/2x for
> 0 ≤ x ≤ 2π

> Write the equation
> of graph shown:
>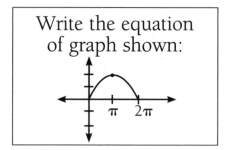

18. Trig Functions and Reference Angles

On each card is a trig function of a negative or non-acute angle, such as **tan 220** or **sin (-50)**. Students are to re-write the given expression as a trig function of a positive acute angle and match up with the person whose answer is the same as theirs. For example, **cos 240** would match up with **cos 120** because both are equal to **-cos 60**.

> Express as the
> function of a positive
> acute angle:
>
> sin 200

> Express as the
> function of a positive
> acute angle:
>
> sin (-20)

19. Inverse Trig Functions

Each card requires students to determine the principal value of an inverse trig function in degrees, such as **Arcsin(1/2)** or **Arctan($\frac{\sqrt{3}}{3}$)**. Students are to match up with the person whose answer is the same as theirs. As an extension to this activity, a new Mix-N-Match can be developed which includes combinations of trig functions and inverse trig functions. For example, **Evaluate sin(Arccos $\frac{\sqrt{3}}{2}$).**

Evaluate:

Arctan (-1)

Evaluate:

Arcsin $\left(\frac{-\sqrt{2}}{2}\right)$

20. Right Triangle Trigonometry

On each student's card is a diagram of a right triangle with the lengths of the sides given. Students are to find the **sine, cosine, tangent, secant, cosecant,** or **cotangent** of the angle marked **x** and express their answer as a fraction in lowest terms. Students are to match up with the person whose problem has the same solution as theirs. For example, the following two cards would be a **match** because they both have an answer of **5/13**...

Find sin x as a fraction in lowest terms

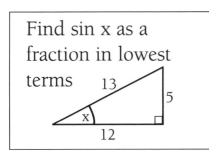

Find cot x as a fraction in lowest terms:

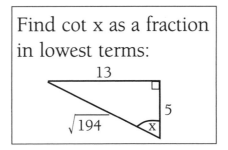

Kagan Publishing • 1 (800) 933-2667
www.KaganOnline.com

MASTERS
Mix-N-Match
Algebra 2

Negative Exponents

OBJECTIVES

Students will re-write monomials with negative exponents in simplest from using only positive exponents.

MATERIALS

Mix-N-Match cards (on the following page), slates or notebooks for students to do scratch work on

DIRECTIONS

Cut out the Mix-N-Match cards and distribute them to students. Students mix (that is, mingle about the classroom) and find a partner to work with. Partners quiz each other regarding the problems on their cards. Once each partner is clear as to the correct answer, partners trade cards and mix again. Students continue to quiz and trade with partners as many times as the teacher sees fit. When the teacher yells, "Freeze! Find your match!" students purposely seek out someone whose problem yields the same answer as theirs and move to the perimeter of the room.

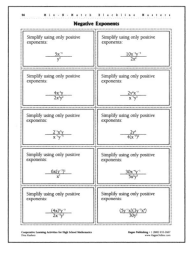

Cooperative Learning Activities for High School Mathematics
Dina Kushnir

Negative Exponents

Simplify using only positive exponents:

$$\frac{5x^{-4}}{y^3}$$

Simplify using only positive exponents:

$$\frac{10x^{-2}y^{-3}}{2x^2}$$

Simplify using only positive exponents:

$$\frac{4x^{-3}y}{2x^3y^2}$$

Simplify using only positive exponents:

$$\frac{2y^2x^{-7}}{x^{-1}y^3}$$

Simplify using only positive exponents:

$$\frac{2^{-1}x^7y}{x^{-1}y^{-5}}$$

Simplify using only positive exponents:

$$\frac{2y^6}{4(x^{-4})^2}$$

Simplify using only positive exponents:

$$\frac{6x(y^{-3})^2}{x^7}$$

Simplify using only positive exponents:

$$\frac{30x^{-4}y^{-1}}{5x^2y^5}$$

Simplify using only positive exponents:

$$\frac{(4x)^0y^{-5}}{2x^{-5}y^3}$$

Simplify using only positive exponents:

$$\frac{(5y^{-1}x)(3y^{-5}x^4)}{30y^2}$$

Negative Exponents

Simplify using only positive exponents:

$$\frac{y^{-2}}{(6x^5)^{-1}}$$

Simplify using only positive exponents:

$$\frac{6x^3y^{-2}}{x^{-2}}$$

Simplify using only positive exponents:

$$\frac{12x^3}{(2x^2)^2y^{-2}}$$

Simplify using only positive exponents:

$$\frac{3x^{-4}y^3}{x^{-3}y}$$

Simplify using only positive exponents:

$$\frac{(3x^{-1})^3}{9x^{-7}y^{-4}}$$

Simplify using only positive exponents:

$$\frac{3xy}{(xy)^{-3}}$$

Simplify using only positive exponents:

$$\frac{(2y)^2x^{-3}}{x^0y^{-1}}$$

Simplify using only positive exponents:

$$\frac{xy^3}{(2x^{-2})^{-2}}$$

Simplify using only positive exponents:

$$\frac{x^{-4}}{(4x)(2y^{-1})}$$

Simplify using only positive exponents:

$$\frac{(2x)^{-3}y^2}{x^2y}$$

Kagan Publishing • 1 (800) 933-2667
www.KaganOnline.com

Cooperative Learning Activities for High School Mathematics
Dina Kushnir

Negative Exponents

Simplify using only positive exponents:

$$\frac{(4x)^{-2}}{y^3}$$

Simplify using only positive exponents:

$$\frac{xy^{-2}}{16x^3y}$$

Simplify using only positive exponents:

$$\frac{(2x^{-3})^2}{yx}$$

Simplify using only positive exponents:

$$\frac{4xy^{-1}}{x^8}$$

Simplify using only positive exponents:

$$\frac{2(x^{-2}y)^2}{xy^2}$$

Simplify using only positive exponents:

$$\frac{8x^{-3}y}{(2x)^2y}$$

Simplify using only positive exponents:

$$\frac{3x^{-2}y}{x^3(y^2)^{-1}}$$

Simplify using only positive exponents:

$$\frac{(9x^{-3})(2xy)}{6y^{-2}x^3}$$

Simplify using only positive exponents:

$$\frac{2x^0y^{-4}}{x^{-3}y^3}$$

Simplify using only positive exponents:

$$\frac{8x^{-4}y^{-2}}{4x^{-7}y^5}$$

Kagan Publishing • 1 (800) 933-2667
www.KaganOnline.com

MASTERS
Mix-N-Match
Trigonometry

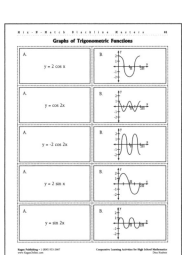

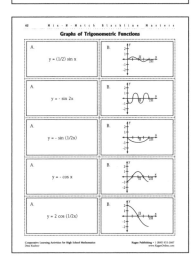

Graphs of Trigonometric Functions

OBJECTIVES

a) Students will sketch a graph of an equation in the form y = asin(bx) or y = acos(bx) based on its amplitude, period, and frequency

b) Students will state the equation of a trigonometric graph.

MATERIALS

Mix-N-Match cards (on the following page), slates or notebooks for students to do scratch work on

DIRECTIONS

Cut out the Mix-N-Match cards and distribute them to students. Half the cards are "A cards" and half are "B cards." Students mix (that is, mingle about the classroom) and find a partner so that there is one "A card" and one "B card" in each pair.

Cooperative Learning Activities for High School Mathematics
Dina Kushnir

Partners quiz each other regarding the problems on their cards. Those with equation cards would would ask their partner to draw a sketch of that equation on their slate (or in their notebook). Those with graph cards would ask their partner to state the equation of the graph shown. Once each partner is clear as to the correct answer, partners trade cards and mix again. Students continue to quiz and trade with partners as many times as the teacher sees fit. When the teacher yells, "Freeze! Find your match!" students purposely seek out their matches. The goal is to get each equation paired with its graph. Students move to the perimeter of the room once they find their "match."

Graphs of Trigonometric Functions

A.

$y = 2 \cos x$

B.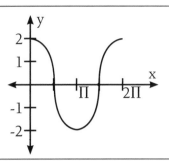

A.

$y = \cos 2x$

B.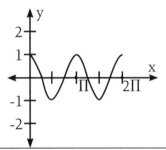

A.

$y = -2 \cos 2x$

B.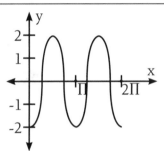

A.

$y = 2 \sin x$

B.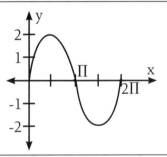

A.

$y = \sin 2x$

B.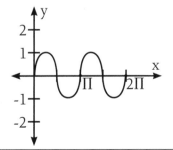

Kagan Publishing • 1 (800) 933-2667
www.KaganOnline.com

Graphs of Trigonometric Functions

A.

$y = (1/2) \sin x$

B.

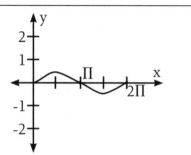

A.

$y = - \sin 2x$

B.

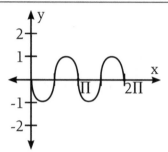

A.

$y = - \sin (1/2x)$

B.

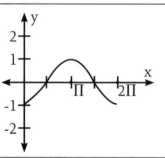

A.

$y = - \cos x$

B.

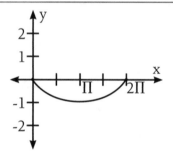

A.

$y = 2 \cos (1/2x)$

B.

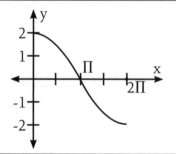

Graphs of Trigonometric Functions

A.

$y = -2 \sin 2x$

B.
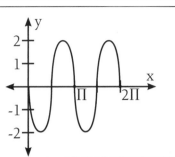

A.

$y = (1/2) \cos x$

B.
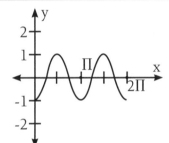

A.

$y = - \cos 2x$

B.
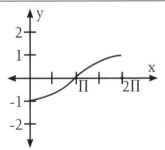

A.

$y = - \cos (1/2x)$

B.
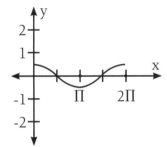

A.

$y = -2 \cos x$

B.
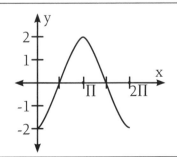

Graphs of Trigonometric Functions

A.

$y = - \sin x$

B.

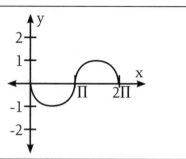

A.

$y = 2 \sin (1/2x)$

B.

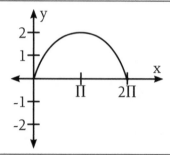

A.

$y = -2 \sin x$

B.

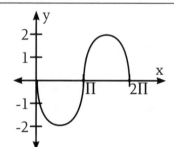

I V I T I E S

Mix-N-Match

Pre-Calculus

1. EVALUATING DETERMINANTS

Each card requires students to find the value of **x** in a problem which involves a 2x2 determinant. Some examples are shown below...

Find the value of x:	Find the value of x:
$\begin{bmatrix} 1 & -4 \\ 3 & -2 \end{bmatrix} = x$	$\begin{bmatrix} 3 & 2 \\ x & 4 \end{bmatrix} = -8$

Students are to match up with the person whose x-value is the same as theirs.

2. ARITHMETIC AND GEOMETRIC PROGRESSIONS

On each card is a problem involving arithmetic or geometric progressions.
For example:

Find the 23rd term in an arithmetic progression where the first term is 5 and the common difference is 3.

Students are to match up with the person whose problem has the same solution as theirs. It is recommended that students be allowed to carry slates and scientific calculators with them for this activity. The problems incorporated into this activity can also include *Sum of an Arithmetic Progression or Sum of a Geometric Progression*.

In an arithmetic progression, the first term is 7 and the 25th term is 19. Find the common difference between each term.	In a geometric progression, the first term is 16 and the 10th term is 1/32. Find the common ratio between each term.

Cooperative Learning Activities for High School Mathematics
Dina Kushnir

3. POLYNOMIAL FUNCTION GRAPHS

Half the cards are **A cards** which contain a polynomial function, such as
$y = (x - 3)^2 (x + 4)$ or $y = 2(x - 1) (x + 2)^2$. The other cards are **B cards** which
contain sketches of the graphs of these polynomial functions. Students are to
match up so that each polynomial function is paired with its graph. An example of
a **match** is shown below...

Sketch the graph of:

$y = 1/2 \ (x+3)(x-2)^2$

Write the equation for
the graph shown:

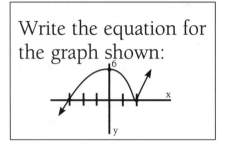

4. CONVERTING EQUATIONS FORM POLAR TO RECTANGULAR FORM (AND VICE VERSA)

Half the cards are **A cards** which contain the equations of graphs in rectangular form,
such as $x^2 + y^2 = 25$ or $3x - 2y = 7$. The other cards are **B cards** which contain the
equations of these graphs in polar form, such as $r^2 = 25$. Students are to match up so
that each rectangular equation is paired with its equivalent polar equation.

Express in
polar form:

$3x + x^2 + y^2 = 10$

Express in
rectangular form:

$3r \ COS \ \theta + r^2 = 10$

5. LAWS OF LOGARITHMS

On each card is a combination of several logarithmic expressions, such as **2log34 - log38**. Students are to apply the laws of logarithms as they re-write the given expression as a single logarithm. They then match up with the person whose answer is the same as theirs. For example, $\log_6 32 - \log_6 2$ would match up with $2\log_6 2 + \log_6 4$ because both are equivalent to $\log_6 16$.

Express as a
single logarithm:

$$\log_5 2 + 2\log_5 3$$

Express as a
single logarithm:

$$2\log_5 3 + \log_5 6 - \log_5 3$$

6. FACTOR THEOREM AND REMAINDER THEOREM

The problem on each card requires students to use the Factor Theorem or the Remainder Theorem. Some examples are ...

Find the remainder when $2x^5 - 3x^3 + 5x^2 + 7x - 6$ is divided by $(x + 2)$.
Find the value of k so that $(x - 3)$ is a factor of $x^4 - 3x^3 + kx^2 - 6x + 8$.

Students are to match up with the person whose problem has the same solution as theirs. It is recommended that students be allowed to carry slates with them for this activity.

Find the remainder
when
$3x^3 + 2x^2 - 5x - 2$
is divided by $(x+2)$

Find K so that $(x-1)$ is
a factor of
$Kx^5 - 5x^4 + 3x^3 - x + 11$

7. BINOMIAL EXPANSION

Half the cards are **A cards** which require students to find a given term of a given binomial expansion. For example, **Find the 3rd term of $(3x + y)^6$** or **Find the middle term of $(p - 2q)^4$**. The other cards are **B cards** which contain the answers to these questions. Students are to match up so that each question is paired with the correct answer.

> Find the 3rd term of
>
> $(2x - 1)^7$

> $672x^5$

8. VENN DIAGRAMS

Half the cards are **A cards** which contain an expression written in set notation, such as **(A∩C) U (B∩C)**. The other cards are **B cards** which contain shaded Venn diagrams of these expressions, such as...

> Sketch the Venn diagram for
>
> $(A \cup B) \cap (A \cap B \cap C)'$

> Give the shading directions for...
>
>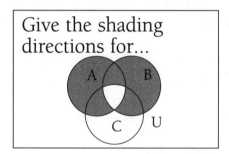

Students are to match up so that each equation is paired with its correct diagram. It is recommended that students be allowed to carry slates with them for this activity.

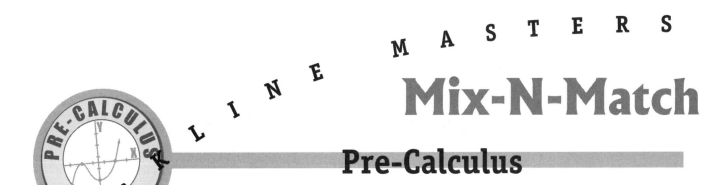

Mix-N-Match
Pre-Calculus

Polynomial Functions and Their Graphs

OBJECTIVES

Students will a) Sketch the graph of a polynomial function, b) determine the equation of a given polynomial function graph

MATERIALS

Mix-N-Match cards (on the following page), slates or notebooks for students to do scratch work on

DIRECTIONS

Cut out the Mix-N-Match cards and distribute them to students. Half the cards are "A cards" and half are "B cards." Students mix (that is, mingle about the classroom) and find a partner so that there is one "A card" and one "B card" in each pair. Partners quiz each other regarding the problems on their cards. Those with equation cards would

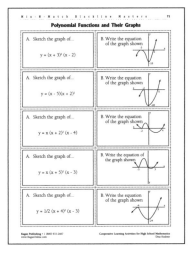

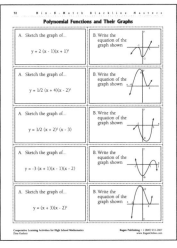

Cooperative Learning Activities for High School Mathematics
Dina Kushnir

ask their partner to draw a rough sketch of that x-intercepts and y-intercepts should be labelled equation on their slate (or in their notebook). Those with graph cards would ask their partner to state the equation of the graph shown. Once each partner is clear as to the correct answer, partners trade cards and mix again. Students continue to quiz and trade with partners as many times as the teacher sees fit. When the teacher yells, "Freeze! Find your match!" students purposely seek out their matches. The goal is to get each equation paired with its graph. Students move to the perimeter of the room once they find their matches.

Polynomial Functions and Their Graphs

A. Sketch the graph of...

$$y = (x + 3)^2 (x - 2)$$

B. Write the equation of the graph shown

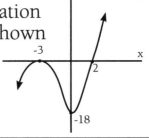

A. Sketch the graph of...

$$y = (x - 5)(x + 2)^2$$

B. Write the equation of the graph shown

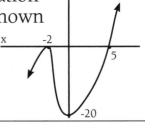

A. Sketch the graph of...

$$y = x (x + 2)^2 (x - 4)$$

B. Write the equation of the graph shown

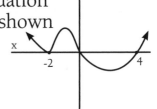

A. Sketch the graph of...

$$y = x (x + 5)^2 (x - 3)$$

B. Write the equation of the graph shown

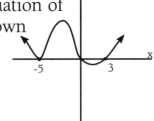

A. Sketch the graph of...

$$y = 1/2 (x + 4)^2 (x - 3)$$

B. Write the equation of the graph shown

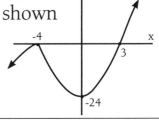

Kagan Publishing • 1 (800) 933-2667
www.KaganOnline.com

Cooperative Learning Activities for High School Mathematics
Dina Kushnir

Polynomial Functions and Their Graphs

A. Sketch the graph of...

$$y = 2\,(x - 1)(x + 1)^2$$

B. Write the equation of the graph shown

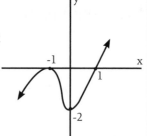

A. Sketch the graph of...

$$y = 1/2\,(x + 4)(x - 2)^2$$

B. Write the equation of the graph shown

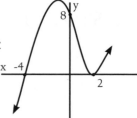

A. Sketch the graph of...

$$y = 1/2\,(x + 2)^2\,(x - 3)$$

B. Write the equation of the graph shown

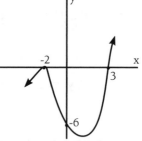

A. Sketch the graph of...

$$y = -3\,(x + 1)(x - 1)(x - 2)$$

B. Write the equation of the graph shown

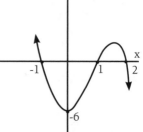

A. Sketch the graph of...

$$y = (x + 3)(x - 2)^2$$

B. Write the equation of the graph shown

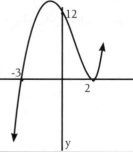

Polynomial Functions and Their Graphs

A. Sketch the graph of...

$$y = x^2 (x - 4)^2$$

B. Write the equation of the graph shown

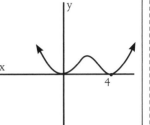

A. Sketch the graph of...

$$y = 2 (x - 2)(x + 3)$$

B. Write the equation of the graph shown

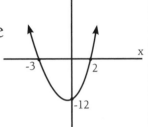

A. Sketch the graph of...

$$y = 3 (x - 1)^2 (x + 1)$$

B. Write the equation of the graph shown

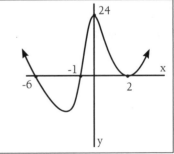

A. Sketch the graph of...

$$y = (x + 6)(x + 1)(x - 2)^2$$

B. Write the equation of the graph shown

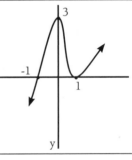

A. Sketch the graph of...

$$y = (x + 1)^2 (x - 5)$$

B. Write the equation of the graph shown

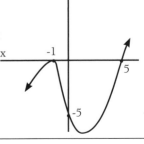

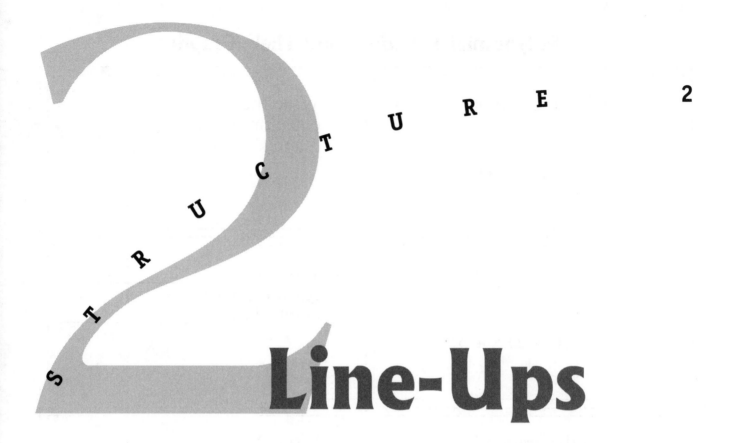

Line-Ups

Steps at a Glance

1. Teacher names a topic or gives student cards to use for lining up.

2. Students line up in order.

3. Teacher announces a discussion topic or question.

4. Students turn to a partner next to them in the line-up to discuss the question or topic, often using Timed Pair Share.

In this structure, the teacher creates an imaginary continuum in the classroom. One end is "highest" and the other is "lowest." Each student is given a card with a number or problem on it. Students evaluate the answer to whatever problem is on their card and then line up in order from least to greatest. Once students are lined up, they then discuss their card and position with a nearby partner. Partners may be formed by pairing up with an adjacent person, or by "folding" the line in half. Within their partnerships, students decide who will be Person A and who will be Person B. Person A shares his/her problem and solution while Person B listens. Person B then gives feedback to Person A and then shares his/her problem and solution. Person A then gives feedback. Once they have shared with a partner, students may then report out to the class.

L I N E - U P S

There are three ways to increase individual accountability among the students. One is to make students commit to their position in the line-up without talking. Then after being allowed to discuss their positions, they may then choose to adjust location. The second way to increase individual accountability is to make students work out the problems on paper while sitting alone at their desks, then lining up once everyone has committed to an answer.

Variation, Student may do a "Mix-Pair-Line-Up" activity. Students mingle around the room and

pair up with a classmate. Partners quiz each other as to the content on their cards and swap cards when done. Students continue to mix and pair until the teacher yells, "Freeze! Line-Up!"

On the next several pages, you will find a list of several ideas for incorporating Line-Ups into the high school mathematics classroom. Following this list are several ready-to-use Line-Up activities with problem cards. Simply reproduce the card sets, cut along the black lines, and distribute the cards to the students.

Line-Ups Contents

PRE-ALGEBRA

- *Activities* 77
- *Blackline Masters* 81

ALGEBRA 1

- *Activities* 87
- *Blackline Masters* 91

GEOMETRY

- *Activities* 97
- *Blackline Masters* 99

ALGEBRA 2

- *Activities* 103

TRIGONOMETRY

- *Activities* 103
- *Blackline Masters* 111

PRE-CALCULUS

- *Activities* 115
- *Blackline Masters* 119

Management Tips

1 Give students adequate solo time or think time.

2 If solving a problem requires a paper-pencil solution, have students carry their scratchwork with them as they line up. This way, it's easier for students to explain their work and find each other's mistakes.

3 This structure works best with short answer questions or problems that only require a few steps.

Social Skills

1 Greeting someone

2 Giving and accepting praise

3 Giving and accepting constructive criticism

4 Asking for help

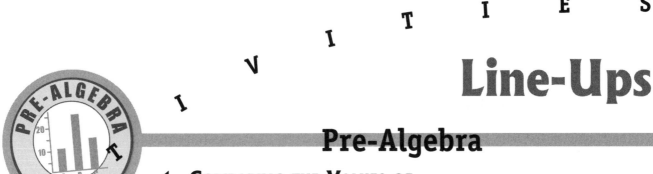

Line-Ups

Pre-Algebra

1. COMPARING THE VALUES OF FRACTIONS, DECIMALS, AND PERCENTS

On each student's card is written either a fraction, a decimal or a percent. (The fractions may even be given as pictures). Students must be able to convert fractions, decimals, and percents to other equivalent forms in order to compare the value of their card to the value of the other cards. Line up from lowest to highest.

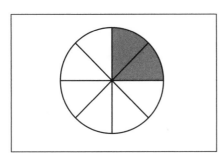

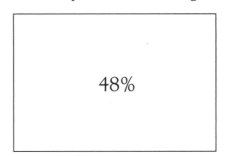

48%

2. AREA, PERIMETER, AND VOLUME

On each student's card is a geometric shape with some given dimensions. Students may line up according to the area, perimeter, surface area, or volume of their figure (as per teacher's direction).

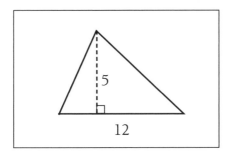

3. STATISTICS

On each students card is a set of numerical data. Students may line up according to the mean, median, or mode of their data (as per teacher's direction).

> 12, 13, 13, 15, 12, 10

pgs. 83-85

4. ORDER OF OPERATIONS

On each student's card is a numeric expressions involving several binary operations. Students evaluate these expressions according to the order of operations and line up according to their answers.

$$\frac{(6 + 2)^2 - 4}{7 - 2}$$

5. ROUNDING

On each student's card is a number. The teacher instructs students, according to his/her discretion, to round the number on their card to the nearest whole number, the nearest ten, the nearest hundred, nearest tenth, etc. Students line up according to their answer.

> 15, 231.08

6. GREATEST COMMON FACTOR/LEAST COMMON MULTIPLE

On each student's card is a list of whole numbers. Students line up according to the GCF or LCM of the numbers on their cards (as per teacher's direction).

> 6, 5, 2

7. OPERATIONS ON FRACTIONS

On each student's card is a pair of fractions, fraction A and fraction B. Students line up according to the value of A + B, A - B, AB, A/B, or B/A (as per teacher's discretion). This activity can also be done with **Decimals** or **Integers**.

> $A = 5\dfrac{2}{3}$
>
> $B = 2\dfrac{1}{5}$

8. PROBLEM SOLVING WITH PROPORTIONS

On each students card is a word problem requiring the student to set up and solve a proportion. Students solve the problems on their cards and line up according to their answers. This activity can also be done with *Percents*.

> If 10 lollipops cost $2.10, find the cost of 7 lollipops.

9. ANGLE MEASUREMENT

On each student's card is the diagram of an angle. Students measure the angle with a protractor and line up according to the measure of the angle.

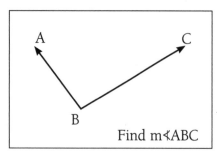

Find m∢ABC

10. THE COUNTING PRINCIPLE

On each student's card is a word problem requiring use of the counting principle. (i.e. **Joe has 5 ties and 3 shirts. How many different shirt-tie combinations can he make?**) Students line up according to their answers. This activity is also useful for practicing **Permutations** and **Combinations**.

Ali has 3 pairs of shoes and 8 pairs of socks. How many different shoe-sock combinations can Ali make?

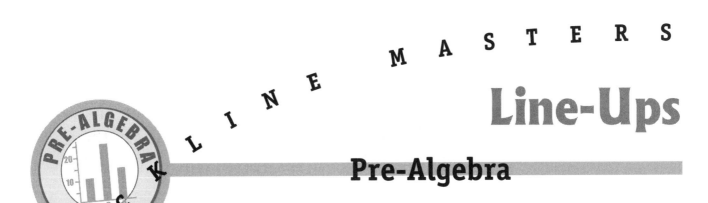

MASTERS

Line-Ups

Pre-Algebra

Order of Operations

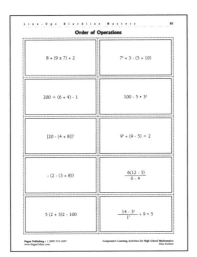

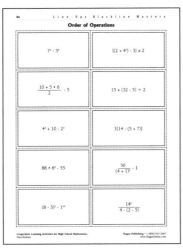

OBJECTIVES

Students will evaluate numeric expressions involving several binary operations.

MATERIALS

Scratch paper, pencils, Line-Up cards (see following pages)

PREREQUISITE LEARNING

Students should be familiar with the correct order of operations in order to do this activity. Some of the cards incorporate operations on negative numbers, so students should be familiar with operations on integers.

FOLLOW-UP QUESTIONS

Is the value of your card a prime number or a composite number?

Is the value of your card a perfect square? A perfect cube?

Is the value of your card divisible by 3?

The above questions can be posed to the whole class, and students can then discuss their answers with a partner next to them. Students can then report out to the class regarding their partner's answer. (i.e.— "My partner's card was worth 14, which is not a prime number.")

POSSIBLE EXTENSIONS

Do subsequent Line-Up activities incorporating decimals and/or fractions (both positive and negative).

Order of Operations

$8 + (9 \times 7) + 2$	$7^2 + 3 - (5 + 10)$
$200 \div (6 + 4) - 1$	$100 - 5 \bullet 3^2$
$[20 - (4 + 8)]^2$	$9^2 + (9 - 5) \div 2$
$- (2 - (3 + 8))$	$\dfrac{6(12 - 3)}{6 - 4}$
$5 (2 + 3)2 - 100$	$\dfrac{14 - 3^2}{1^7} + 9 \bullet 5$

Order of Operations

$7^2 - 3^0$

$[(2 + 4^2) - 3] \times 2$

$$\frac{10 + 5 \cdot 6}{2} - 5$$

$15 + (32 - 5) \div 2$

$4^2 + 10 - 2^3$

$3[14 - (5 + 7)]$

$88 \cdot 6^0 - 55$

$$\frac{50}{(4 + 1)^2} - 1$$

$(8 - 3)^2 - 1^{10}$

$$\frac{14^0}{4 - (2 - 5)}$$

Order of Operations

$$\frac{(10 - 4)^2}{2 + 7^0}$$

$$15 - [3 - (2 + 1)^2]$$

$$(4 + 2 \bullet 3)^2$$

$$60 - (42 - 1) \div 5$$

$$16 - (3 + 1)^2$$

$$\frac{20 - 1 - 3}{3 + 2^0}$$

$$[25 - (2 + 6) + 3] \div 2$$

$$\frac{61 - 5^2}{4 \bullet 3}$$

$$17 - 2^4 + (10 - (-3))$$

$$35 - \frac{(2 + 1)^3}{3}$$

Line-Ups

Algebra 1

1. EVALUATING ALGEBRAIC EXPRESSION

On each student's card is an algebraic expression and the values of the variables involved in the expression. Students evaluate their expression and line up according to their answers.

pgs. 93-95

Evaluate $h^2 - 2jk$ when
$h = -4$, $j = 3$ and $k = 5$

2. LINEAR EQUATIONS IN ONE VARIABLE

On each student's card is an algebraic equation in one variable. The complexity of the equations can vary depending on where the students are in their mastery of solving equations. They can include one or several steps, parentheses, variables on both sides of the equation, etc. Students solve the equations on their cards and line up according to their answers.

Solve for x:

$$3(x + 1) = 4x - 8$$

Cooperative Learning Activities for High School Mathematics
Dina Kushnir

3. QUADRATIC EQUATIONS

On each student's card is a quadratic equation. Students solve the equations on their cards by factoring, and then line up according to the *sum* (or *product*) of the roots.

Solve for x:

$$x^2 - 3x = 18$$

4. LINEAR EQUATIONS IN TWO VARIABLES

On each student's card is the equation of a line. Students are to get the equation into $y = mx + b$ form and line up according to the slope (or y-intercept) of their lines.

$$5x - 2y = 20$$

5. ALGEBRA WORD PROBLEMS

One each student's card is a word problem which requires students to establish a variable, write an equation, and solve the equation. Students line up according to their solutions.

Joe has 5 more marbles than Sue. If Joe and Sue have 21 marbles all together, how many marbles does Sue have.

6. Solving Systems of Equations

On each student's card is a system of two linear equations in two variables, x and y. Students solve the system of equations algebraically, and then line up according to the sum (or product) of x and y.

$$5x - 2y = 11$$
$$3x + y = 11$$

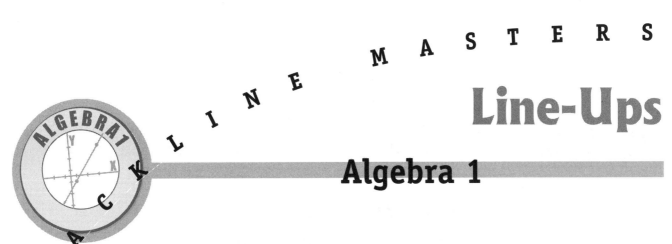

Line-Ups

Algebra 1

Evaluating Algebraic Expressions

OBJECTIVES

Students will evaluate algebraic expressions by using substitution.

MATERIALS

Scratch paper, pencils, Line-Up cards (see following pages)

PREREQUISITE LEARNING

Students should be able to perform operations on integers according to the correct order of operations

FOLLOW-UP QUESTIONS

How could you adjust the algebraic expression on your card so that the resulting value would be 2? Can you come up with two or three different ways to do this?

Let x = 4 and y = -3. Write three different algebraic expressions using x and/or y which are worth -1.

Cooperative Learning Activities for High School Mathematics
Dina Kushnir

The above questions can be posed to the whole class, and students can then discuss their answers with a partner next to them. Students can then report out to the class regarding their **partner's** answer, or write their answer down on paper to hand in.

POSSIBLE EXTENSIONS

Students can make up their own Line-Up cards with an algebraic expression and a given list of variables. Do another Line-Up using the student-made cards.

Evaluating Algebraic Expressions

The value of $4x^2 - 5$ when
$x = 3$

The value of $5(y + 4) - 3x$ when
$x = 2$ and $y = 4$

The value of $3(x + 2)^2$ when
$x = -4$

The value of $\frac{1}{2}(B + b)h$
when $B = 3$, $b = 5$ and $h = 4$

The value of $-5x + 4 + 2y$ when
$x = 2$ and $y = 5$

The value of $x^2 + 4x - 6$
when $x = -5$

The value of $\frac{7x + 5}{x - 1}$ when $x = 3$

The value of $2(x - 3)^2 + 5x$
when $x = -1$

The value of $9y^2 - 4x$ when
$x = -4$ and $y = 1$

The value of $7 - 3x + 5m$
when $x = -6$ and $m = 4$

Kagan Publishing • 1 (800) 933-2667
www.KaganOnline.com

Cooperative Learning Activities for High School Mathematics
Dina Kushnir

Evaluating Algebraic Expressions

The value of $m^3 + 3(x + 2)$
when m = -2 and x = 4

The value of $(2y)^2 + 4y$
when y = -3

The value of -7(m + 4) -3b
when m = -1 and b = -8

The value of $5h + 5^2$
when h = -6

The value of $6k^3 + 3d$
when k = -1 and d = -2

The value of 5(b + 4) + 4b
when b = -1

The value of $\dfrac{(4 + x)^2}{x - 1}$ when x = 6

The value of $\dfrac{4x^2}{x + 4}$ when x = -2

The value of $\dfrac{4 + 7}{x - 2} + 3$ when x = 5

The value of 5m - (6x - 3)
when m = 8 and x = 4

Evaluating Algebraic Expressions

The value of $3(x - 2)^3 + x$
when $x = 4$

The value of $-5y^3 + 6k$
when $y = -2$ and $k = 1$

The value of $5(x - 3) \div 2 + 3m$
when $x = 9$ and $m = -2$

The value of $6(h - 3)^2 + 5v$
when $v = -5$ and $h = 6$

The value of $8c + \dfrac{x - 2}{3}$
when $c = 4$ and $x = 20$

The value of $\dfrac{5x^2 + m^0}{2}$
when $x = -3$ and $m = 6$

The value of $\dfrac{1}{3}(2x)^2$
when $x = 6$

The value of $6(f - r^3)$
when $f = 1$ and $r = -2$

The value of $6h \div (x - 4) + 5$
when $h = 3$ and $x = 6$

Find the value of $-x^3 + 2y$
when $x = -2$ and $y = 5$

Line-Ups

Geometry

1. INTERIOR AND EXTERIOR ANGLES OF A POLYGON

On each card is a geometric figure with some given information. Students are to find the measure of the angle marked "x" in the diagram and line up according to their answers.

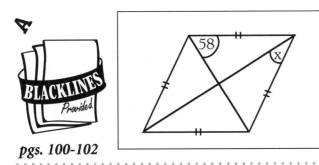

pgs. 100-102

2. LENGTHS OF SEGMENTS

On each student's card is a diagram with some given information. Students are to find the length of the segment marked **x** and line up according to their answers. Finding the value of **x** may involve application of the ***Pythagorean Theorem, Special Right Triangle Ratios, Properties of Various Quadrilaterals, Similar Triangles***, or ***Circle Theorems***.

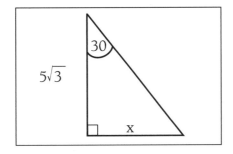

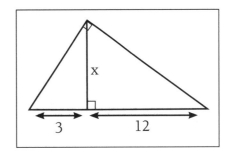

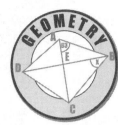

3. CIRCLE THEOREMS

On each student's card is a diagram involving a circle, some line segments, and some given information. By applying the various circle theorems, students are to find the measure of the arc, angle, or line segment marked **x** and line up according to their answers.

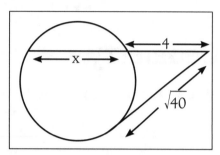

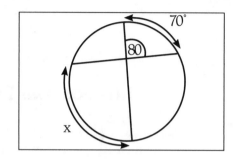

4. COORDINATE GEOMETRY

On each student's card is a pair of points. Students may line up according to either a) the distance between the two points or b) the slope of the line segment connecting the two points.

P(-5, 3)

Q(0, 7)

The slope of $\overline{PQ}$ is

_____

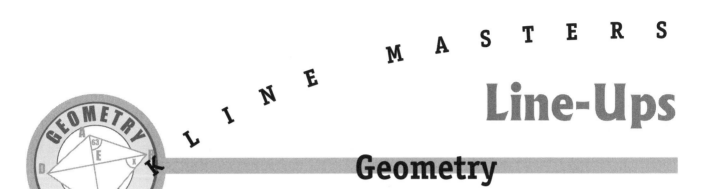

Line-Ups

Geometry

Angle Measures

OBJECTIVES

Students will find the measure of an angle in a geometric figure based on given information

MATERIALS

Scratch paper, pencils, geometry Line-Up cards (see following pages)

PREREQUISITE LEARNING

Students should know the properties of the various polygons (parallelograms, rhombuses, rectangles, squares, trapezoids, isosceles trapezoids, isosceles triangles). They should also be familiar with the relationships governing the interior angles of any regular n-gon.

POSSIBLE EXTENSIONS

Have students create their own geometry problems on index cards. If desired, divide students into groups with given criteria. For example, Group A must use a quadrilateral in their drawings, Group B must use only triangles, etc. Do another line-up using the student-made cards.

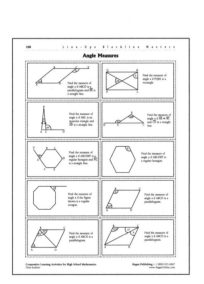

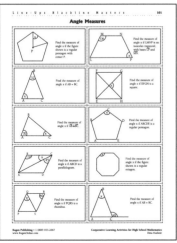

Angle Measures

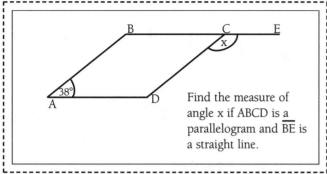

Find the measure of angle x if ABCD is a parallelogram and $\overline{BE}$ is a straight line.

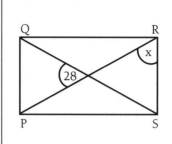

Find the measure of angle x if PQRS is a rectangle.

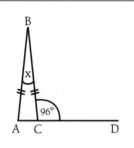

Find the measure of angle x if ABC is an isosceles triangle and $\overline{AD}$ is a straight line.

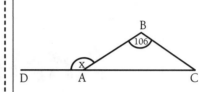

Find the measure of angle x if $\overline{AB} \cong \overline{BC}$ and $\overline{CD}$ is a straight line.

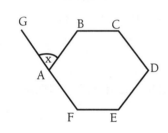

Find the measure of angle x if ABCDEF is a regular hexagon and $\overline{FG}$ is a straight line.

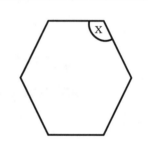

Find the measure of angle x if ABCDEF is a regular hexagon.

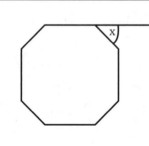

Find the measure of angle x if the figure shown is a regular octagon.

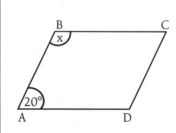

Find the measure of angle x if ABCD is a parallelogram.

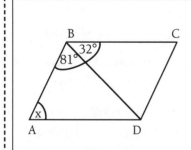

Find the measure of angle x if ABCD is a parallelogram.

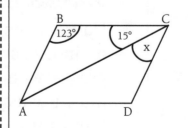

Find the measure of angle x if ABCD is a parallelogram.

Cooperative Learning Activities for High School Mathematics
Dina Kushnir

Kagan Publishing • 1 (800) 933-2667
www.KaganOnline.com

Angle Measures

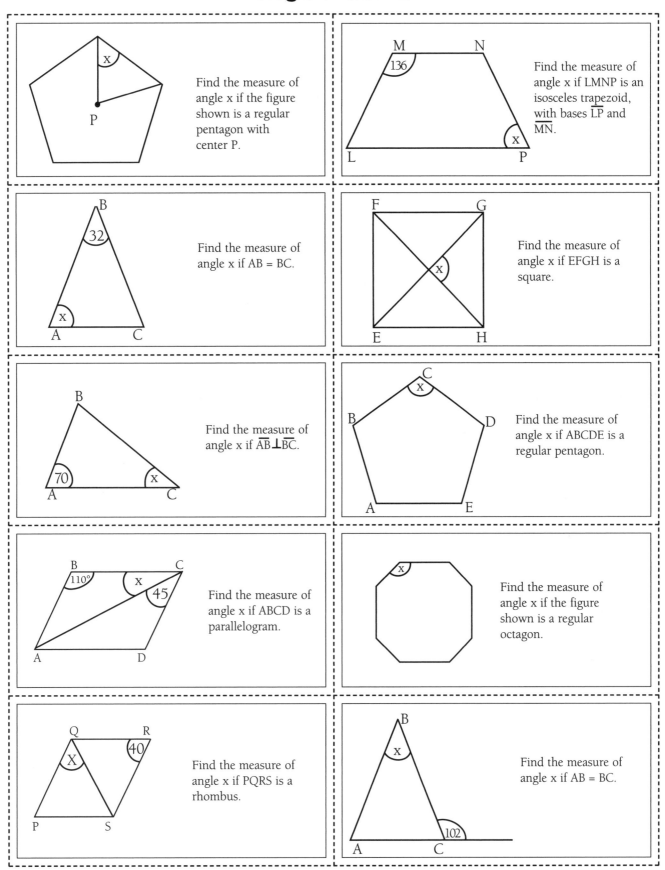

Find the measure of angle x if the figure shown is a regular pentagon with center P.

Find the measure of angle x if LMNP is an isosceles trapezoid, with bases LP and MN.

Find the measure of angle x if AB = BC.

Find the measure of angle x if EFGH is a square.

Find the measure of angle x if AB⊥BC.

Find the measure of angle x if ABCDE is a regular pentagon.

Find the measure of angle x if ABCD is a parallelogram.

Find the measure of angle x if the figure shown is a regular octagon.

Find the measure of angle x if PQRS is a rhombus.

Find the measure of angle x if AB = BC.

Kagan Publishing • 1 (800) 933-2667
www.KaganOnline.com

Cooperative Learning Activities for High School Mathematics
Dina Kushnir

Angle Measures

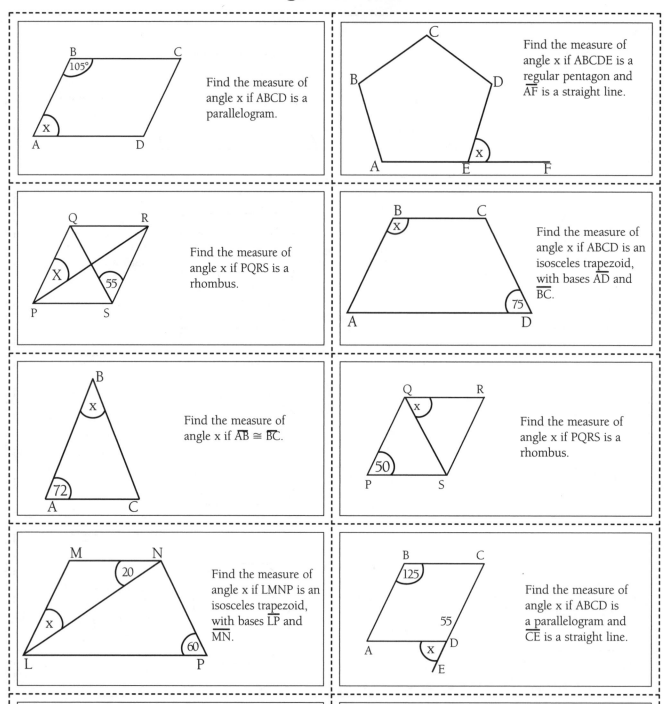

Find the measure of angle x if ABCD is a parallelogram.

Find the measure of angle x if ABCDE is a regular pentagon and $\overline{AF}$ is a straight line.

Find the measure of angle x if PQRS is a rhombus.

Find the measure of angle x if ABCD is an isosceles trapezoid, with bases $\overline{AD}$ and $\overline{BC}$.

Find the measure of angle x if $\overline{AB} \cong \overline{BC}$.

Find the measure of angle x if PQRS is a rhombus.

Find the measure of angle x if LMNP is an isosceles trapezoid, with bases $\overline{LP}$ and $\overline{MN}$.

Find the measure of angle x if ABCD is a parallelogram and $\overline{CE}$ is a straight line.

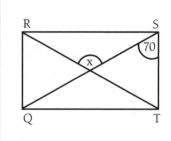

Find the measure of angle x if QRST is a rectangle.

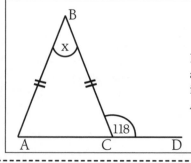

Find the measure of angle x if ABC is an isosceles triangle and $\overline{AD}$ is a straight line.

Line-Ups

Algebra 2 and Trigonometry

1. ABSOLUTE VALUE EQUATIONS/RADICAL EQUATIONS

On each student's card is an absolute value equation. Students solve the equations and line up according to their answers. This activity can also be done with *Rational Equations* and *Radical Equations* of varying degrees of difficulty. Since some of these types of equations may have more than one answer, students may line up according to the *sum* of their solutions or the larger of the two solutions.

$$|3x + 5| = 17$$

$$\sqrt{x + 5} - 7 = 2$$

2. EVALUATING FUNCTIONS

On each student's card is a rule for f(x) and a given value of x. Students evaluate f(x) and line up according to their answers. This activity can be extended to include Compositions of Functions (see suggested activity #3).

$$f(x) = \sqrt{x + 7}$$

$$x = 9$$

Cooperative Learning Activities for High School Mathematics
Dina Kushnir

3. COMPOSITIONS OF FUNCTIONS

On each student's card is a rule for f(x), a rule for g(x) and a given value of x. Students line up according to the value of f(g(x)), g(f(x)), f(f(x)), or g(g(x)), according to the teacher's discretion.

$$f(x) = 2x + 1$$

$$g(x) = x^2 - 5$$

$$x = 3$$

4. INVERSE OF A FUNCTION

On each student's card is a given f(x) and a given value of x. Students line up according to the value of $f^{-1}(x)$.

$$f(x) = 3x + 7$$

$$x = 19$$

Find $f^{-1}(x)$

5. WRITING THE EQUATION OF A LINE

On each student's card is a given slope, m, and a given point P. Students write the equation of the line with slope m and passing through P. Students then line up according to the y-intercept of their equation. This activity can be modified so that each student's card has two points, P and Q, written on it. Students must write the equation of the line passing through both P and Q. Many other modifications of this activity are possible, including writing the equation of a line that is parallel or perpendicular to a given line and passes through a given point.

Write the equation of the line with slope 3/5 and passing through P(-10, 2)

P(7, -1) Q(0, 5) Write the equation of $\overline{PQ}$

6. Writing Quadratic Equations

On each student's card is a pair of numbers, x_1 and x_2. Students are to write a quadratic equation in the form $ax^2 + bx + c = 0$ whose solution set is $\{x_1, x_2\}$. Students line up according to the value of "b" in their answer. This activity can also be extended to include roots that are complex, such as $\{2 + 3i, 2 - 3i\}$.

$X_1 = 4$ and $X_2 = -3$.

Write the quadratic equation whose roots are X_1 and X_2. Write your answer in $ax^2 + bx + c = 0$ form.

---

7. Direct Variation

On each student's card is a statement such as, **X varies directly as Y. If Y = 2 when X = 5, find X when Y = 7.** Students line up according to their answers. Problems involving *Inverse Variation* can also be used, either instead of or in addition to the direct variation problems.

---

x varies directly as y. If x = 6
when y = 4 find y when x = 15

---

8. Undefined Fractions

On each student's card is a rational expression involving the variable **x**. Students find the value of x which makes the fraction undefined. If there is more than one possible solution for x, students may line up according to the sum of their answers or according to the largest answer.

For what value of x is the expression
$$\frac{3x + 1}{2x - 10}$$ undefined?

9. REPEATING DECIMALS

On each student's card is a repeating decimal. Students are to convert that decimal into a fraction in *lowest terms*, then line up according to the *denominator* in their fractional answer.

> Express $.\overline{12}$ as a fraction in **lowest terms**.

10. QUADRATIC FORMULA

On each student's card is a quadratic equation that cannot be solved by factoring. Students are to use the quadratic formula to find the roots of the equation and convert their answers to decimals. Students line up according to the value of the greater root.

> Solve $x^2 - 4x + 7 = 0$ using the quadratic formula. Express your final answers as decimals rounded to the nearest 100th.

11. PARABOLAS

On each student's card is an equation in the form $y = ax^2 + bx + c$. Students line up according to the y - value of the turning point for the given parabola.

> $y = 2x^2 - 4x + 3$

12. LOGARITHMS

On each student's card is a log expression, such as $\log_3 27$. Students line up according to the value of their expressions.

Evaluate

$$\log_2 \left(\frac{1}{8}\right)$$

13. EXPONENTIAL AND LOGARITHMIC EQUATIONS

On each student's card is an equation, such as $\log_3 x - \log_3(2x + 5) = 1$. Students solve their equations and line up according to their answers.

$$\log_3 x = \log_3 5 + \log_3 8$$

$$4^{x+3} = 8^{2x-5}$$

14. FINDING ANGLE MEASURES USING TRIGONOMETRIC FUNCTIONS

Given the quadrant of ∡ B and one trig function value of ∡ B, students find the measure of ∡ B to the nearest degree and line up according to their answers.

pgs. 112-114

∠B terminates in QIII
sinB = -8/15
Find m∠B to the
nearest degree

Cooperative Learning Activities for High School Mathematics
Dina Kushnir

15. FINDING SEGMENT LENGTHS USING RIGHT TRIANGLE TRIGONOMETRY

On each student's card is a right triangle with one given acute angle and one given side. Using a trig function, students write an equation to find the side marked **x** to the nearest tenth. Students line up according to their answers.

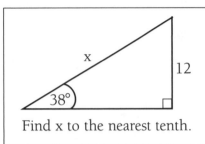

Find x to the nearest tenth.

16. REFERENCE ANGLES

On each student's card is an angle measure (either positive or negative). Students line up according to the reference angle of their given angle.

State the reference angle for 216°

17. UNDERSTANDING RADIAN MEASURE

On each student's card is a diagram of a circle with a given radius and an angle, X, which intercepts a given arc. Student's are to find the measure of angle X in radians and line up according to their answers. This activity can be modified so that students must work backwards to find either the radius of the circle or the length of the intercepted arc.

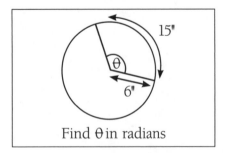

Find θ in radians

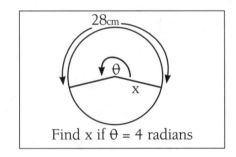

Find x if θ = 4 radians

18. RADIAN AND DEGREE MEASURE

On each student's card is an angle in radians. Students convert their angles to degrees and line up according to their answers.

$$\theta = \frac{7\pi}{5}$$

Find θ in degrees

19. ANGLE SUM AND ANGLE DIFFERENCE FORMULAS

On each student's card are given values for sin A and cos B. Students are to use the given information to evaluate sin (A + B), sin (A - B), cos (A + B), cos (A - B), etc., according to the teacher's directions. Students line up according to their answers. This activity can be modified to include the *Angle Product Formulas, Double Angle Formulas* or *Half-Angle Formulas*.

sin A = -4/5
cos B = 1/2
Evaluate cos (A - B)

20. SOLVING TRIGONOMETRIC EQUATIONS

On each student's card is a given trig equation, such as 8sinX - 2 = 1. Students solve for X to the nearest degree and line up according to their answers. Since there will often be more than one solution for X in these types of equations, the teacher may have the students line up according to the largest value of X in their solution set.

4 tan x - 5 = 6

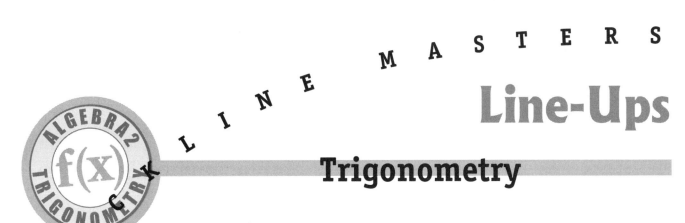

Line-Ups

Trigonometry

Finding Angle Measures Using All Six Trig Functions

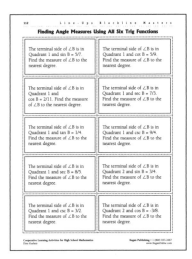

OBJECTIVES

Given the quadrant of angle B, and one trigonometric function value of angle B, students will find the measure of angle B to the nearest degree.

MATERIALS

Paper, pencils, geometry Line-Up cards (see following pages), scientific calculators

PREREQUISITE LEARNING

Students should be familiar with all six trigonometric functions, and their relationship to the unit circle. Students should be able to identify the location of all four quadrants. Finally, students should be able to use a scientific calculator to evaluate trig functions and inverse trig functions.

Finding Angle Measures Using All Six Trig Functions

The terminal side of ∠B is in Quadrant 1 and sin B = 5/7. Find the measure of ∠B to the nearest degree.	The terminal side of ∠B is in Quadrant 1 and cot B = 5/9. Find the measure of ∠B to the nearest degree.
The terminal side of ∠B is in Quadrant 1 and cos B = 2/11. Find the measure of ∠B to the nearest degree.	The terminal side of ∠B is in Quadrant 1 and sec B = 7/3. Find the measure of ∠B to the nearest degree.
The terminal side of ∠B is in Quadrant 1 and tan B = 1/4. Find the measure of ∠B to the nearest degree.	The terminal side of ∠B is in Quadrant 1 and csc B = 9/4. Find the measure of ∠B to the nearest degree.
The terminal side of ∠B is in Quadrant 1 and sec B = 8/5. Find the measure of ∠B to the nearest degree.	The terminal side of ∠B is in Quadrant 2 and sin B = 3/4. Find the measure of ∠B to the nearest degree.
The terminal side of ∠B is in Quadrant 1 and csc B = 3/2. Find the measure of ∠B to the nearest degree.	The terminal side of ∠B is in Quadrant 2 and cos B = -3/8. Find the measure of ∠B to the nearest degree.

Finding Angle Measures Using All Six Trig Functions

The terminal side of ∠B is in Quadrant 2 and tan B = -7/2. Find the measure of ∠B to the nearest degree.

The terminal side of ∠B is in Quadrant 2 and cot B = -2/17. Find the measure of ∠B to the nearest degree.

The terminal side of ∠B is in Quadrant 2 and sec B = -7/3. Find the measure of ∠B to the nearest degree.

The terminal side of ∠B is in Quadrant 3 and sin B = -4/11. Find the measure of ∠B to the nearest degree.

The terminal side of ∠B is in Quadrant 2 and csc B = 9/2. Find the measure of ∠B to the nearest degree.

The terminal side of ∠B is in Quadrant 3 and cos B = -7/19. Find the measure of ∠B to the nearest degree.

The terminal side of ∠B is in Quadrant 2 and cot B = -12/7. Find the measure of ∠B to the nearest degree.

The terminal side of ∠B is in Quadrant 3 and tan B = 15/28. Find the measure of ∠B to the nearest degree.

The terminal side of ∠B is in Quadrant 2 and sec B = -14/9. Find the measure of ∠B to the nearest degree.

The terminal side of ∠B is in Quadrant 3 and sec B = -23/12. Find the measure of ∠B to the nearest degree.

Finding Angle Measures Using All Six Trig Functions

The terminal side of ∠B is in Quadrant 3 and csc B = -17/3. Find the measure of ∠B to the nearest degree.

The terminal side of ∠B is in Quadrant 4 and sin B = - 8/21. Find the measure of ∠B to the nearest degree.

The terminal side of ∠B is in Quadrant 3 and cot B = 16/5. Find the measure of ∠B to the nearest degree.

The terminal side of ∠B is in Quadrant 4 and tan B = -12/19. Find the measure of ∠B to the nearest degree.

The terminal side of ∠B is in Quadrant 3 and a cos B = -2/7. Find the measure of ∠B to the nearest degree.

The terminal side of ∠B is in Quadrant 4 and cot B = -30/13. Find the measure of ∠B to the nearest degree.

The terminal side of ∠B is in Quadrant 3 and tan B = 11/6. Find the measure of ∠B to the nearest degree.

The terminal side of ∠B is in Quadrant 4 and sec B = 20/3. Find the measure of ∠B to the nearest tenth.

The terminal side of ∠B is in Quadrant 4 and cos B = 5/17. Find the measure of ∠B to the nearest degree.

The terminal side of ∠B is in Quadrant 4 and csc B = -18/13. Find the measure of ∠B to the nearest degree.

Kagan Publishing • 1 (800) 933-2667
www.KaganOnline.com

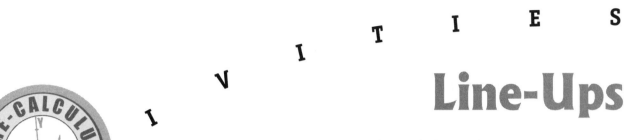

Line-Ups

Pre-Calculus

1. DETERMINANTS

On each student's card is a 2x2 or a 3x3 determinant. Students evaluate the determinant and line up according to their answers.

Evaluate
$\begin{bmatrix} 3 & -7 \\ 2 & 5 \end{bmatrix}$

Find x if
$\begin{bmatrix} x & -8 \\ 2 & 3 \end{bmatrix} = 22$

pgs. 121-123

2. ARITHMETIC AND GEOMETRIC PROGRESSIONS

On each card is a series of four numbers. Students are to decide whether the given series is an arithmetic or geometric progression, and then find the nth term of that progression. Students line up according to their answers.

Find the 26th term of the
progression 3.1, 3.7, 4.3, 4.9, ...

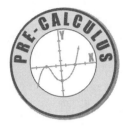

3. Sum of an Arithmetic or Geometric Series

On each student's card is a series of four numbers and a given value of n. Students are to decide whether the series is an arithmetic or geometric progression, and then find the sum of the first n terms in that progression. Students line up according to their answers.

> Find the sum of
> the first 8 terms of
> the progression
>
> 4, 2, 1, 1/2,...

4. Remainder Theorem

On each student's card is a given polynomial, P(x), and a given factor, f. Students use the remainder theorem to determine the remainder when P(x) is divided by f, then line up according to their answer.

> Find the remainder when
>
> $P(x) = x^5 - 3x^3 + 2x + 7$ is divided by (x + 2)

5. Matrices

On each student's card are given two matrices, A and B. According to the teacher's direction, students may be asked to compute, A + B, AB, A^2, 3B - A, etc. Students are then asked to line up according to a certain number in the resulting matrix. For example, they might line up based on the number in the "lower right - hand corner" of their answer matrix.

$$A = \begin{bmatrix} 3 & 2 & 5 \\ 1 & -4 & 6 \end{bmatrix} \qquad B = \begin{bmatrix} 0 & 1 \\ 5 & 3 \\ -2 & 8 \end{bmatrix}$$

6. DISTANCE FROM A POINT TO A LINE

On each student's card is a point and the equation of a line. Students find the distance from the given point to the given line and line up according to their answers.

> Find the distance from (2, -3) to the line 3x - 4y = 10.

7. ANGLE OF INCLINATION

On each student's card is the equation of a line. Students are to find the angle of inclination of that line to the nearest degree and line up accordingly.

> Find the angle of inclination of the line -5y + 7 = 3x to the nearest degree

8. SUMMATION

Given an expression in sigma notation, such as $\sum\limits_{k=1}^{5} (k-1)^2$, students are to compute the given sum and line up accordingly.

> Evaluate
>
> $2 \sum\limits_{n=2}^{5} 3n-5$

Kagan Publishing • 1 (800) 933-2667
www.KaganOnline.com

Cooperative Learning Activities for High School Mathematics
Dina Kushnir

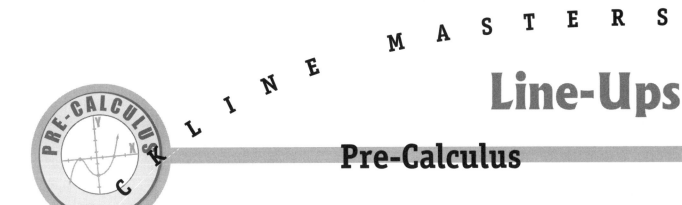

Line-Ups

Pre-Calculus

Arithmetic and Geometric Progressions

OBJECTIVES

Students will determine the nth term of an arithmetic or geometric progression given the first 4 terms in the progression.

MATERIALS

Paper, pencils, pre-calculus Line-Up cards (see following pages), scientific calculators

PREREQUISITE LEARNING

Students should be able to determine whether a given sequence is a geometric or arithmetic progression. They should also be familiar with the formulas used to find the nth term of each type of sequence.

POSSIBLE EXTENSIONS

Students can form pairs, trade cards, and then find

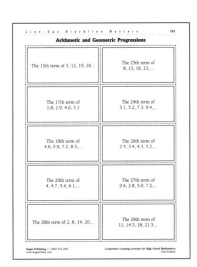

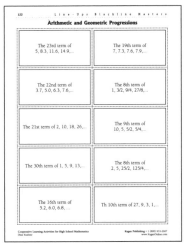

the SUM of the first "n" terms of the sequences on their cards. (The teacher can decide on the value of "n"). Students should be familiar with the formulas for the sum of an arithmetic and/or geometric progression.

Arithmetic and Geometric Progressions

The 15th term of
5, 12, 19, 26,...

The 25th term of
8, 13, 18, 23,...

The 17th term of
1.8, 2.9, 4.0, 5.1,...

The 24th term of
3.1, 5.2, 7.3, 9.4,...

The 18th term of
4.6, 5.9, 7.2, 8.5,...

The 26th term of
2.5, 3.4, 4.3, 5.2,...

The 20th term of
4, 4.7, 5.4, 6.1,...

The 27th term of
0.6, 2.8, 5.0, 7.2,...

The 28th term of
2, 8, 14, 20,...

The 29th term of
11, 14.5, 18, 21.5,...

Arithmetic and Geometric Progressions

The 23rd term of
5, 8.3, 11.6, 14.9,...

The 19th term of
7, 7.3, 7.6, 7.9,...

The 22nd term of
3.7, 5.0, 6.3, 7.6,...

The 8th term of
1, 3/2, 9/4, 27/8,...

The 21st term of 2, 10, 18, 26,...

The 9th term of
10, 5, 5/2, 5/4,...

The 30th term of 1, 5, 9, 13,...

The 8th term of
2, 5, 25/2, 125/4,...

The 16th term of
5.2, 6.0, 6.8,...

The 10th term of 27, 9, 3, 1,...

Arithmetic and Geometric Progressions

The 10th term of
36, 24, 16, 32/3,...

The 8th term of
2/25, 1/5, 1/2, 5/4,...

The 9th term of
48, 12, 3, 3/4,...

The 10th term of 1, 4, 16, 64,...

The 8th term of
144, 36, 9, 9/4,...

The 10th term of 2, 8, 32, 128,...

The 10th term of
1/2, 3/2, 9/2, 27/2,...

The 9th term of 81, 27, 9, 3,...

The 8th term of 2/9, 2/3, 2, 6,...

The 9th term of 81, 54, 36, 24,...

Kagan Publishing • 1 (800) 933-2667
www.KaganOnline.com

Cooperative Learning Activities for High School Mathematics
Dina Kushnir

Inside-Outside Circle

Steps at a Glance

1. Students stand as a class in one large circle.

2. Students form pairs. In each pair, one student steps to the inside of the circle facing his or her partner on the outside. The class is now in two concentric circles.

3. Inside circle students ask a question from their question card; outside circle students answer. Inside circle students praise or coach. (Alternative: the teacher asks a question and designates who is to share). Partners switch roles: Outside circle students ask, listen, then praise or coach.

4. Partners trade question cards.

5. Inside circle students rotate clockwise to a new partner. (The teacher may call rotation numbers: "Rotate Three Ahead." The class may do a "choral count" as they rotate).

In this structure, students form two concentric circles, with equal numbers of students in each circle. Students are to stand face-to-face with a partner, one person from the inside circle and one from the outside circle. The circles rotate according to the teacher's instructions. For example, "Outside circle move three people to the right." Students are then face to face with a new partner. Partners take turns asking each other questions, quizzing each other with flashcards, sharing some information, or answering questions posed by the teacher. If flashcards are used, student partners may swap cards once they are done quizzing each other. The circles rotate again and students again form new partners. The process may be repeated as many times as the teacher sees fit. If there is an odd number of students, have two students travel around the circle together OR have the teacher participate in the activity.

An extension of this activity is to have students create their own flashcards. The teacher can set guidelines about the content and level of difficulty of the problems on the cards.

On the following pages is an extensive, but certainly not exhaustive, list of ideas for using Inside-Outside Circle. Flashcards for some of these activities are also included. To use the flashcards, simply duplicate the appropriate

cards, and *cut* along all the *horizontal* lines. Then *fold* along the *vertical* lines so that the answers to the questions are hidden.

This structure works best when the problems being solved do not require lengthy paper - pencil solutions. This structure is more conducive to short - answer or higher level thinking questions that can be answered verbally. Depending on the computations and steps required, teachers may encourage students to carry scientific calculators or slates with them during an Inside-Outside Circle activity.

Inside-Outside Circle Contents

PRE-ALGEBRA

- Activities 127
- Blackline Masters 135

ALGEBRA 1

- Activities 143
- Blackline Masters 147

GEOMETRY

- Activities 157
- Blackline Masters 161

ALGEBRA 2

- Activities 169
- Blackline Masters 177

TRIGONOMETRY

- Activities 169
- Blackline Masters 177

PRE-CALCULUS

- Activities 193
- Blackline Masters 197

Inside-Outside Circle

Management Tips

1 Forming two concentric circles with students is trickier than you'd think. Even with high school students, simply instructing them to "Form two concentric circles" does not work. Here is a way to make it easier…
a. Students create one large circle.
b. Students choose a partner next to them.
c. One partner moves inside the circle.
d. Partners face each other.

2 It is easier to monitor students if the teacher stands inside the two concentric circles.

3 Have students indicate they are done quizzing each other by having them both face the teacher in the center.

4 Rotate circles with specific commands. For example, "Outside circle move three people to the left" or "Inside circle move two people to the right."

5 This structure works best with questions that do not require paper and pencil solutions, such as short-answer mastery questions or higher level thinking questions.

Social Skills

1 Greeting others

2 Giving and accepting praise

3 Giving and accepting constructive criticism

4 Coaching others

5 Departing gambits

I T I E S

V

I

Inside-
Outside Circle
Pre-Algebra

1. AREA AND PERIMETER

Students are given a figure with labeled segment lengths. They then quiz each other on the area and/or perimeter of the figure. This activity can be extended to include circumference and area of a circle.

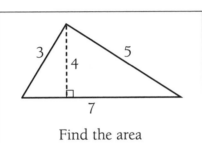

Find the area

A = 14 sq. un.

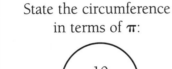
State the circumference
in terms of π:

C = 10π

2. PLACE VALUE

Students are given a number or decimal. They quiz each other on place value. For example, "Which digit is in the tens place?"

| 7,425.27 | 1000's place : 7
hundreds place : 4
tens place : 2
ones place : 5
tenths place : 2
hundredths place : 7 |

3. ROUNDING

Given a number or decimal, students quiz each other on rounding to a given place value. For example, "Round this number to the nearest tenth."

| 560.72 | To nearest 100 : 600
To nearest 10 : 560
To nearest whole # : 561
To nearest 10th : 560.7 |

4. GREATEST COMMON FACTOR AND LEAST COMMON MULTIPLE

Given a list of two or more whole numbers, students quiz each other on the GCF and/or LCM of the numbers.

| 27, 3, 9 | LCM : 27
GCF : 3 |

5. ORDER OF OPERATIONS

Given a numeric expression involving several operations, students quiz each other on the value of the given expression. For example, $5^2 - 32$ or $3(14 - 6)$.

$17 - 2 \bullet 8 + 5^2$	26

6. PROPERTIES OF ARITHMETIC

Given a number sentence, students quiz each other on the property demonstrated. Properties may include commutative, associative, distributive, identity properties, and inverse properties.

$7 + (3 + 2) = (7 + 3) + 2$	associative property of addition

7. OPERATIONS ON INTEGERS

Students quiz each other on the sum, difference, product, or quotient of two given integers. This activity can be extended to include several operations simultaneously, thereby requiring knowledge of the order of operations. This activity can also be modified to include fractions and/or decimals.

-15 3	sum : -12 difference : -18 product : -45 quotient : -5

8. COMPARING FRACTIONS

Students quiz each other on which of two given fractions is greater. This activity can be modified for decimals, or a combination of fractions and decimals.

Which is greater: $\frac{5}{8}$ or $\frac{3}{5}$	$\frac{5}{8}$

9. CONVERTING FRACTIONS, DECIMALS, AND PERCENTS

Students are given a fraction, decimal or percent. They must then convert their number to one of the other two forms. For example: "Convert 5.3 to a fraction" or "Express 56% as a fraction in lowest terms."

Express $\frac{7}{2}$ as a decimal	3.5

10. INTERPRETING DATA AND GRAPHS

Students are given a graph or other data display. They then quiz each other on the information presented in the display. For example: "What was the total sales volume for the year 1987?" or "Who ate the most jelly beans?" or "During what months did the average temperature exceed 70° F?"

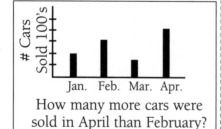

How many more cars were sold in April than February?	100

11. SIMPLIFYING ALGEBRAIC EXPRESSIONS

Given an algebraic expression, students quiz each other on simplifying the expression.

Simplify: $7x^2 + x - 5x^2 - 12x$	$2x^2 - 11x$

12. OPERATIONS ON MONOMIALS

Given two algebraic monomials, students quiz each other on the sum, difference, product, or quotient of these monomials.

Express as a single fraction in lowest terms: $\dfrac{7}{2b} + \dfrac{5}{4}$	$\dfrac{14 + 5b}{4b}$

13. INEQUALITY GRAPHS

Given a graph on a number line, students quiz each other on the equation of the graph. For example:

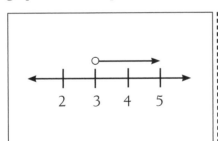

$x > 3$

More advanced versions of inequality graphs can also be used, such as the one shown.

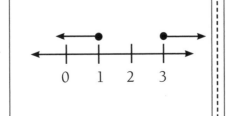

$(x \leq 1) \text{ or } (x \geq 3)$

Cooperative Learning Activities for High School Mathematics
Dina Kushnir

14. PERCENTS

Students quiz each other on finding a given percent of a given number. For example: "What is 20% of 80?"

(*Blackline masters for this activity are included in this chapter.)

pgs. 136-141

What is 15% of 120?	18

15. CONVERTING UNITS

Students quiz each other on converting one unit of measurement to another. For example: "How many feet are in 3 miles?" Students should be allowed to carry calculators with them for this activity.

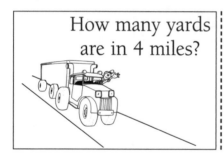

How many yards are in 4 miles?

7,040 yards

16. SYMMETRY

Students quiz each other on whether a given figure has line symmetry, point symmetry, or rotational symmetry.

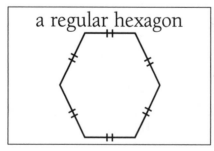

a regular hexagon

line sym: yes
point sym: yes
rotational sym: yes

17. SIMPLE ONE-STEP EQUATIONS

Students quiz each other on the solutions to simple equations, such as 5x = -25 or x - 6 = 13.

Solve for x: x + 12 = 5	x = -7

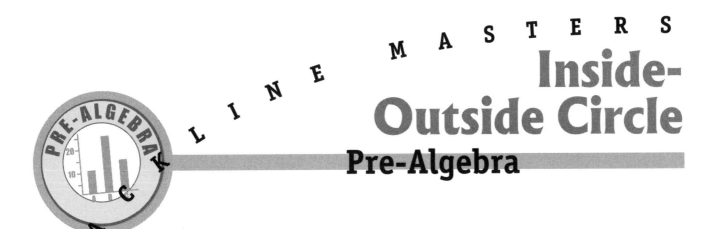

Percent Problems

OBJECTIVES

Students will determine a given percent of a given number, preferably without a calculator

MATERIALS

Inside-Outside Circle flashcards (see following pages)

PREREQUISITE LEARNING

Students should be able to determine 10% of a number, and use this to find other percent multiples of 5 (such as 5%, 15%, 20%, 25%,…)

FOLLOW-UP QUESTIONS

Once students have mastered finding a percent of a number, they can then attempt other types of percent problems. For example, "20% of a number is 12. Find the number." or "15 is what percent of 40?"

Percent Problems

What is 60% of 20?	12
What is 70% of 500?	350
What is 65% of 80?	52
What is 80% of 30?	24
What is 85% of 40?	34

Cooperative Learning Activities for High School Mathematics
Dina Kushnir

Kagan Publishing • 1 (800) 933-2667
www.KaganOnline.com

Percent Problems

What is 90% of 300?	270
What is 5% of 40?	2
What is 110% of 60?	66
What is 105% of 60?	63
What is 110% of 20?	22

Percent Problems

What is 50% of 28?	14
What is 15% of 40?	6
What is 20% of 320?	64
What is 30% of 50?	15
What is 35% of 60?	21

Percent Problems

What is 40% of 400?	160
What is 25% of 120?	30
What is 45% of 80?	36
What is 55% of 100?	55
What is 60% of 400?	240

Percent Problems

What is 30% of 210?	63
What is 40% of 600?	240
What is 20% of 10?	2
What is 25% of 300?	75
What is 35% of 20?	7

Percent Problems

What is 15% of 500?	75
What is 5% of 160?	8
What is 15% of 800?	120
What is 105% of 40?	42
What is 110% of 120?	132

Inside-Outside Circle
Algebra 1

1. Writing Algebraic Expressions

Given a verbal phrase, students quiz each other on translating the phrase into algebraic form. For example: "5 more than p" or "twice n."

6 less than half of r	$\frac{1}{2} r - 6$

2. Operations on Polynomials

Given two algebraic polynomials, students quiz each other on the sum, difference, product, or quotient of these polynomials.

Subtract $x^2 + 5$ from $3x^2 - x + 1$	$2x^2 - x - 4$

Kagan Publishing • 1 (800) 933-2667
www.KaganOnline.com

Cooperative Learning Activities for High School Mathematics
Dina Kushnir

3. FACTORING

Students quiz each other on factoring a given polynomial.

(*Blackline masters for this activity are included in this chapter.)

pgs. 149-155

Factor $x^2 - x - 12$	$(x - 4)(x + 3)$

4. SLOPE OF A LINE

Students quiz each other on the slope of a given line which is graphed on a coordinate plane.

Find the slope of the line shown: 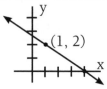	$\dfrac{-2}{3}$

5. IRRATIONAL NUMBERS

Given a radical expression, such as $\sqrt{18}$, students must state between which two consecutive integers the given radical lies.

Between which two consecutive integers does $\sqrt{29}$ lie?	Between 5 and 6.

6. SIMPLIFYING RADICALS

Given a radical expression, such as $\sqrt{27}$, students quiz each other on expressing the given radical in simplest radical form.

Express in simplest radical form $\sqrt{40}$	$2\sqrt{10}$

7. COMPLETING THE SQUARE

Given a binomial in the form $ax^2 + bx$, students will add a number to this binomial which will result in a perfect square. For example: "Replace the question mark in $x^2 - 6x + ?$ so that the trinomial is a perfect square."

Fill in the blank to complete the square: $x^2 - 8x +$ _____	16

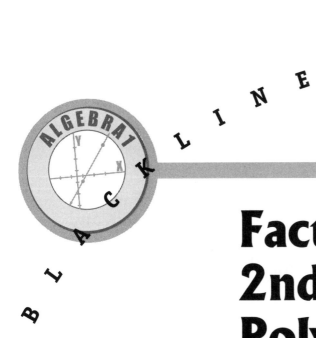

Inside-Outside Circle

Algebra 1

Factoring 2nd Degree Polynomials

(or Multiplying Polynomials and Monomials)

OBJECTIVES

Students will factor polynomials

MATERIALS

Inside-Outside Circle flashcards (next page)

PRE-REQUISITE LEARNING

Factoring out a GCF, recognizing and factoring the difference of two squares, factoring trinomials in the form $ax^2 + bx + c$, where $a = 1$.

FOLLOW-UP ACTIVITY

Once students have mastered the factoring techniques inherent in this activity, they may then attempt more difficult factoring problems. For example, students may be asked to factor

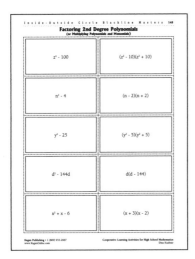

Cooperative Learning Activities for High School Mathematics
Dina Kushnir

trinomials in the form $ax^2 + bx + c$ where $a \neq 1$, such as $2x^2 - 3x - 2$. They may also be asked to "factor completely" polynomials which require more than one step, such as $x^3 - x$ or $5x^2 + 5x - 60$.

NOTE

The flashcards on the following pages may also be used for **multiplying monomials and polynomials.** Just use the factored expressions as the "questions" and the polynomials as the "answers."

Factoring 2nd Degree Polynomials
(or Multiplying Polynomials and Monomials)

$z^4 - 100$	$(z^2 - 10)(z^2 + 10)$
$n^2 - 4$	$(n - 2)(n + 2)$
$y^4 - 25$	$(y^2 - 5)(y^2 + 5)$
$d^2 - 144d$	$d(d - 144)$
$x^2 + x - 6$	$(x + 3)(x - 2)$

Kagan Publishing • 1 (800) 933-2667
www.KaganOnline.com

Cooperative Learning Activities for High School Mathematics
Dina Kushnir

Factoring 2nd Degree Polynomials
(or Multiplying Polynomials and Monomials)

$y^2 - 2y - 3$	$(y - 3)(y + 1)$
$m^2 - 2m - 8$	$(m - 4)(m + 2)$
$d^2 - 2d - 35$	$(d - 7)(d + 5)$
$z^2 - z - 20$	$(z - 5)(z + 4)$
$x^2 - 4x - 12$	$(x - 6)(x + 2)$

Factoring 2nd Degree Polynomials
(or Multiplying Polynomials and Monomials)

$y^2 + 6y - 16$	$(y + 8)(y - 2)$
$m^2 - 6m - 27$	$(m - 9)(m + 3)$
$x^2 - 7x + 12$	$(x - 4)(x - 3)$
$y^2 - 6y + 5$	$(y - 5)(y - 1)$
$d^2 - 9d + 14$	$(d - 7)(d - 2)$

Factoring 2nd Degree Polynomials
(or Multiplying Polynomials and Monomials)

$z^2 - 12z + 27$	$(z - 9)(z - 3)$
$x^2 - 3x$	$x(x - 3)$
$3y^2 - 6y$	$3y(y - 2)$
$z^2 - 5yz^3$	$z^2(1 - 5yz)$
$x^3 - 6x^2$	$x^2(x - 6)$

Factoring 2nd Degree Polynomials
(or Multiplying Polynomials and Monomials)

$5p^3 - 25p$	$5p(p^2 - 5)$
$3x - 6y - 9$	$3(x - 2y - 3)$
$ax^2 + ab$	$a(x^2 + b)$
$5x - 15$	$5(x - 3)$
$x^2 + 5x + 6$	$(x + 3)(x + 2)$

Factoring 2nd Degree Polynomials
(or Multiplying Polynomials and Monomials)

$y^2 + 9y + 18$	$(y + 6)(y + 3)$
$m^2 + 10m + 25$	$(m + 5)(m + 5)$
$d^2 + 11d + 18$	$(d + 9)(d + 2)$
$x^2 + 10x + 21$	$(x + 7)(x + 3)$
$y^2 + 11y + 10$	$(y + 10)(y + 1)$

Factoring 2nd Degree Polynomials
(or Multiplying Polynomials and Monomials)

$n^2 + 12n + 32$	$(n + 8)(n + 4)$
$z^2 + 7z + 10$	$(z + 5)(z + 2)$
$y^2 - 1$	$(y - 1)(y + 1)$
$9 - m^2$	$(3 - m)(3 + m)$
$g^6 - 64$	$(g^3 - 8)(g^3 + 8)$

Kagan Publishing • 1 (800) 933-2667
www.KaganOnline.com

Cooperative Learning Activities for High School Mathematics
Dina Kushnir

Inside-Outside Circle
Geometry

1. GEOMETRY DEFINITIONS

Students quiz each other on the meanings of various terms used in geometry. Students may be asked to define a given word, for example "Define complimentary angles." Or they may be asked to refer to a given diagram and fill in a sentence. For example...

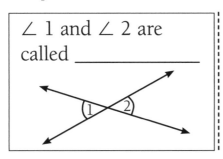

∠ 1 and ∠ 2 are called _____

vertical angles

2. BEGINNING GEOMETRY PROOFS

Given a diagram and some given information, students must draw a conclusion and justify it with a geometry definition.

(*Blackline masters for this activity are included in this chapter.)

pgs. 163-168

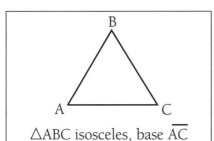

△ABC isosceles, base $\overline{AC}$

$\overline{AB} \cong \overline{BC}$
(def. of isosceles triangle)

3. TRUTH VALUE OF A GIVEN STATEMENT

Students must determine whether a given statement is always, sometimes, or never true. For example: "A square has 4 right angles," or "A triangle has two congruent sides."

A rhombus is a square	Sometimes

4. FINDING ANGLE MEASURES

Given a geometric drawing with some given angle measurements, students must find the measure of the angle marked "x." For example...

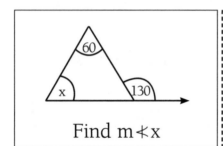

Find m ∢ x

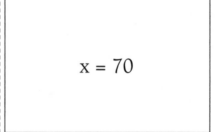

x = 70

5. CONGRUENT TRIANGLES

Given two triangles with some congruent corresponding parts, students must state whether or not the triangles are congruent. If so, they must state the postulate used to prove them congruent, such as SSS, SAS, etc.

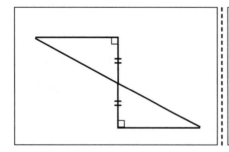

The △'s are congruent by ASA ≅ ASA.

6. PROPERTIES OF QUADRILATERALS

Students are given a property of a quadrilateral and must state all the types of quadrilaterals which have that property. For example, "I have congruent diagonals. I could be a _____." Appropriate responses to these types of problems could include parallelogram, rhombus, square, rectangle, trapezoid, isosceles trapezoid, and kite.

<u>Both</u> pairs of my opposite sides are congruent. I could be a _____.

Square Rectangle Rhombus Parallelogram

7. SPECIAL RIGHT TRIANGLES (30-60-90 TRIANGLES AND 45-45-90 TRIANGLES)

Given a 30 - 60 - 90 or 45 - 45 - 90 triangle and the length of one side, students will find the length of the side marked x in simplest radical form. For example...

Find the value of x:

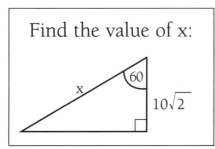

$x = 20\sqrt{2}$

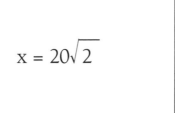

8. TRANSFORMATIONAL GEOMETRY

Students quiz each other on the image of a given point under a given transformation. For example, "What is the image of (4, 7) under a reflection in the y-axis?"

State the image of (8, -6) under a dilation of $\frac{1}{2}$

(4, -3)

M A S T E R S

Inside-Outside Circle
Geometry
Beginning
Geometry Proofs
(Using Geometry Definitions)

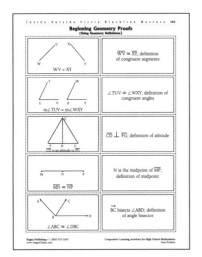

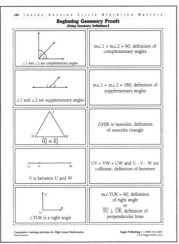

OBJECTIVES

Given a diagram and some information about the diagram, students will draw a conclusion based on that information and state the reason for their conclusion.

MATERIALS

Inside-Outside Circle Flashcards (see following pages)

PRE-REQUISITE LEARNING

Students should be able to define the following terms...

collinear	between
midpoint	angle bisector
segment bisector	complementary angles
supplementary angles	isosceles triangle
vertical angles	linear pair separate line
right angle	perpendicular lines
isosceles trapezoid	right triangle
median of a triangle	congruent segments
congruent angles	altitude

Kagan Publishing • 1 (800) 933-2667
www.KaganOnline.com

Cooperative Learning Activities for High School Mathematics
Dina Kushnir

FOLLOW-UP ACTIVITY

As students progress in their learning of geometry definitions, postulates, and theorems, more advanced Inside-Outside Circle activities can be developed. Students may be given two or three steps to a short proof, and then determine the last step. Some examples are shown below...

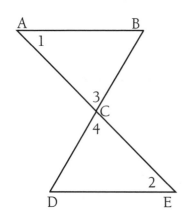

Statements	Reasons
1. ∠1 and ∠2 are supplementary	given
2. ∠3 and ∠4 are supplementary	given
3. ∠1 ≅ ∠3	given
4._____	_____

(ans: ∠2 ≅ ∠4, because ≅ angles have ≅ supplements)

Statements	Reasons
1. ∠1 ≅ ∠2	given
2. $\overline{BC}$ ≅ $\overline{DC}$	given
3. ∠3 and ∠4 are vertical angles	given
4. ∠3 ≅ ∠4	vertical angles are ≅
5._____	_____

(ans: △ABC ≅ △EDC by the AAS postulate)

Beginning Geometry Proofs
(Using Geometry Definitions)

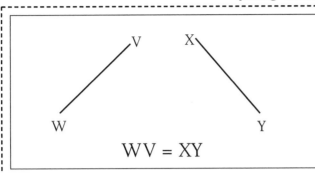

$\overline{WV} \cong \overline{XY}$; definition of congruent segments

WV = XY

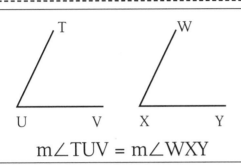

$\angle TUV \cong \angle WXY$; definition of congruent angles

m∠TUV = m∠WXY

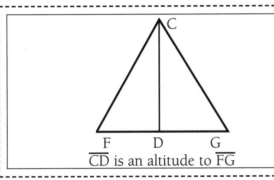

$\overline{CD}$ is an altitude to $\overline{FG}$

$\overline{CD} \perp \overline{FG}$; definition of altitude

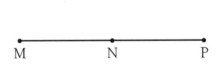

$\overline{MN} \cong \overline{NP}$

N is the midpoint of $\overline{MP}$; definition of midpoint

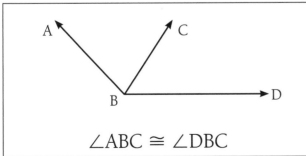

$\angle ABC \cong \angle DBC$

$\overrightarrow{BC}$ bisects $\angle ABD$; definition of angle bisector

---

Kagan Publishing • 1 (800) 933-2667
www.KaganOnline.com

Cooperative Learning Activities for High School Mathematics
Dina Kushnir

Beginning Geometry Proofs
(Using Geometry Definitions)

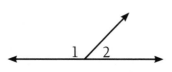

∠1 and ∠2 are complementary angles

m∠1 + m∠2 = 90; definition of complementary angles

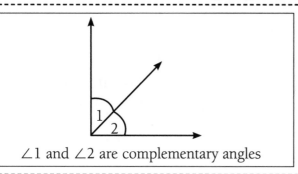

∠1 and ∠2 are supplementary angles

m∠1 + m∠2 = 180; definition of supplementary angles

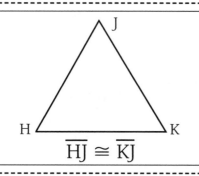

$\overline{HJ} \cong \overline{KJ}$

△HJK is isosceles; definition of isosceles triangle

V is between U and W

UV + VW = UW and U - V - W are collinear; definition of between

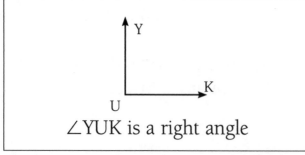

∠YUK is a right angle

m∠YUK = 90; definition of right angle
or
$\overline{YU} \perp \overline{UK}$; definition of perpendicular lines

Beginning Geometry Proofs
(Using Geometry Definitions)

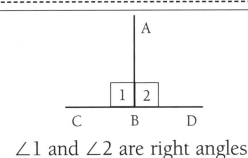

∠1 and ∠2 are right angles

$\overline{AB} \perp \overline{CD}$; definition of
perpendicular lines
or
m∠1 = 90 and m∠2 = 90;
definition of right angle

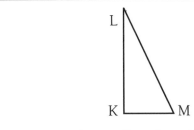

∠K is a right angle. Therefore △KLM is...

△KLM is a right triangle;
definition of right triangle

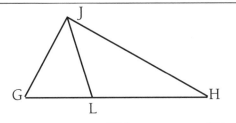

L is the midpoint of $\overline{GH}$. Therefore, $\overline{JL}$ is a...

$\overline{JL}$ is a median of △JGH;
definition of median of a triangle

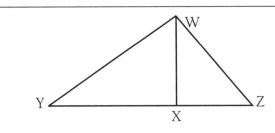

$\overline{WX} \perp \overline{YZ}$. Therefore, $\overline{WX}$ is a(n)...

$\overline{WX}$ is an altitude of
△WYZ; definition
of altitude of a triangle

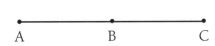

B is the Midpoint of $\overline{AC}$.

$\overline{AB} \cong \overline{BC}$; definition of midpoint.

Kagan Publishing • 1 (800) 933-2667
www.KaganOnline.com

Cooperative Learning Activities for High School Mathematics
Dina Kushnir

Beginning Geometry Proofs
(Using Geometry Definitions)

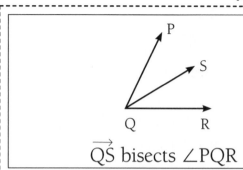

$\overrightarrow{QS}$ bisects $\angle PQR$

∠PQS ≅ ∠SQR; definition of angle bisector

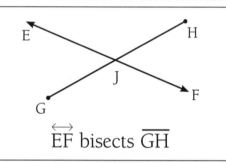

$\overleftrightarrow{EF}$ bisects $\overline{GH}$

J is the midpoint of $\overline{GH}$; definition of segment bisector

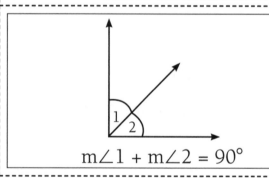

m∠1 + m∠2 = 90°

∠1 and ∠2 are complimentary; definition of complimentary angles

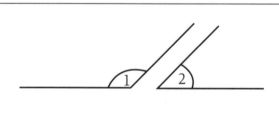

m∠1 + m∠2 = 180°

∠1 and ∠2 are supplementary; definition of supplementary angles

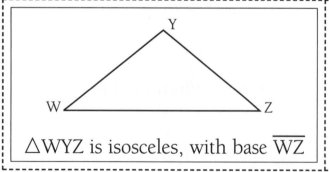

△WYZ is isosceles, with base $\overline{WZ}$

$\overline{WY} \cong \overline{ZY}$; definition of isosceles triangle

Beginning Geometry Proofs
(Using Geometry Definitions)

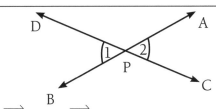

$\overrightarrow{PC}$ and $\overrightarrow{PD}$ are opposite rays;
$\overrightarrow{PA}$ and $\overrightarrow{PB}$ are opposite rays.

∠1 and ∠2 are vertical angles;
definition of vertical angles

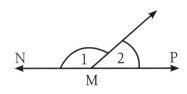

$\overrightarrow{MN}$ and $\overrightarrow{MP}$ are opposite rays.

∠1 and ∠2 form a linear pair;
definition of a linear pair

JK + KL = JL; J - K - L collinear

K is between J and L;
definition of between

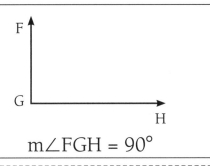

m∠FGH = 90°

∠FGH is a right angle;
definition of a right angle

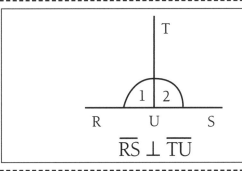

$\overline{RS} \perp \overline{TU}$

∠1 and ∠2 are right angles;
definition of perpendicular lines

Kagan Publishing • 1 (800) 933-2667
www.KaganOnline.com

Cooperative Learning Activities for High School Mathematics
Dina Kushnir

Beginning Geometry Proofs
(Using Geometry Definitions)

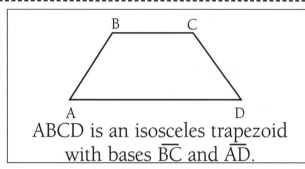

ABCD is an isosceles trapezoid with bases $\overline{BC}$ and $\overline{AD}$.

$\overline{AB} \cong \overline{CD}$; definition of isosceles trapezoid
or
$\overline{BC}$ is parallel to $\overline{AD}$; definition of trapezoid

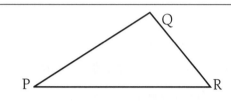

△PQR is a right triangle, with hypotenuse $\overline{PR}$

∠Q is a right angle; definition of right triangle

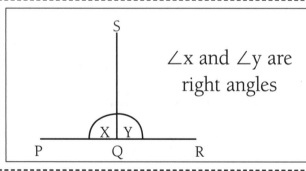

$\overline{KM}$ is a median of △JKL.

M is the midpoint of $\overline{JL}$; definition of median of a triangle

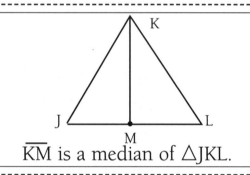

∠x and ∠y are right angles

$\overline{SQ} \perp \overline{PR}$; definition of perpendicular lines; or
m∠x = m∠y = 90, definition of right angle

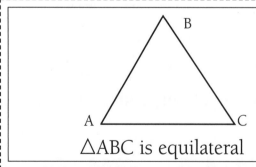

△ABC is equilateral

$\overline{AB} \cong \overline{BC} \cong \overline{AC}$; definition of equilateral △.

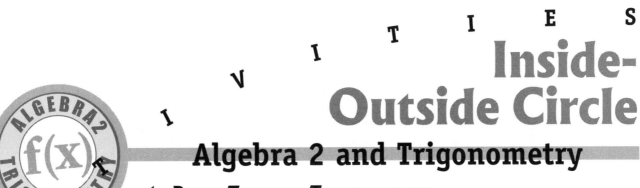

Inside-Outside Circle
Algebra 2 and Trigonometry

1. RIGHT TRIANGLE TRIGONOMETRY

Given a right triangle ABC whose sides are labeled with their lengths, students must express sinA, cosA, tanA, sinB, cosB, or tanB as a fraction.

Express cot B as a fraction...

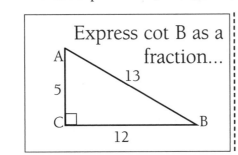

$$\cot B = \frac{12}{5}$$

2. EVALUATING ABSOLUTE VALUE EXPRESSIONS

Given an absolute value expression, such as $2|10-17| + 6$, students quiz each other on the value of the given expression.

Evaluate

$6 + 5\,|\,3 - 12\,|\,-19$

32

3. Identifying Functions

Students quiz each other as to whether or not a given relation is a function. The relation may be given as an equation, a set of ordered pairs, or as a graph on the coordinate plane.

Is $x^2 + 2y^2 = 10$ a function?	No (It is the equation of an ellipse, which does not pass the "vertical line test.")

4. Domain and Range of a Function

Given a function, students quiz each other on the domain and/or range of the function. The function may be given as an equation, as a set of ordered pairs, or as a graph on the coordinate plane.

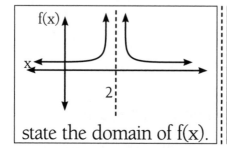

state the domain of f(x).	$\{x \mid x \text{ is real}, x \neq 2\}$ or "all real numbers except 2"

5. Rational Expressions

Given two rational expressions, such as $\frac{7}{x^2y}$ and $\frac{8}{3yx}$ students quiz each other on the least common denominator of the two rational expressions.

What is the LCD of $\frac{3}{5x}$ and $\frac{x^2}{10}$	10x

6. Imaginary Numbers (Powers of "i")

Given an imaginary expression, such as $5i^8 - 7i^3$, students must state the expression in a + bi form.

Express $5i^7 + 3i^2 - 4i$ in a + bi form.	-3 - 9i

7. Fractional and Negative Exponents

Given an expression involving fractional and/or negative exponents, such as or 3^{-2}, students must evaluate these expressions in simplest fractional and/or radical form.

Express in simplest fractional form: $8^{\frac{-2}{3}}$	$\dfrac{1}{4}$

8. Operations on Complex Numbers

Given two numbers in a + bi form, students quiz each other on the sum, difference, or product of the given complex numbers.

Subtract 8 - 2i from 3 + 11i	-5 + 13i

9. Graphs of Quadratic Functions (Parabolas)

Given an equation in the form $y = ax^2 + bx + c$, students determine whether the given function is a parabola opening upward or downward, and whether the turning point is a maximum or a minimum point. This activity can be extended so that students are asked to determine the equation of the axis of symmetry.

$y + 7x = x^2 - 5$	parabola opens upward; turning point is a minimum.

10. Equations of Circles

Given the equation of a circle in standard form, students quiz each other on the center and/or radius of the circle.

state the radius of the circle whose equation is $(x + 5)^2 + y^2 = 17$	radius $= \sqrt{17}$

11. Evaluating Logarithms

BLACKLINES *Provided*

pgs. 187-192

Students quiz each other on evaluating logarithms, such as $\log_9 81$ or $\log .001$.

Evaluate $\log_5 625$	4

12. LAWS OF LOGARITHMS

Students are given statements involving logarithms and must determine whether the statement is true or false based on the laws of logarithms.

For example: "$\log_2 8 = \log_2 4 + \log_2 2$" or "$\log_{10} 9 = \log_9 10$," etc.

True or false: $\log_5 18 - \log_5 6 = \log_5 3$	True

13. TRIG FUNCTIONS IN ALL FOUR QUADRANTS

Given a trig function value, such as sin 235 or tan 83, students must determine whether the trig function value is positive, negative, or zero.

Is cos 215 positive, negative, or zero?	negative

14. TRIG FUNCTION VALUES FOR SPECIAL ANGLES

Given a trig function of a special angle, such as Cos 45, Sin270, or Tan 300, students must state its value in simplest fractional/radical form.

(*Blackline masters for this activity are included in this chapter.)

State the exact value of cos 135	$\dfrac{-\sqrt{2}}{2}$

pgs. 179-184

15. PERMUTATIONS AND COMBINATIONS (WORD PROBLEMS)

Students quiz each other on word problems involving permutations and combinations, such as "How many selections of three books can be made from a pile of 8 books?" or "How many ways can a President and Vice President be chosen from a club of 10 people?" Students should be allowed to carry scientific calculators for this activity.

| How many committees of 5 can be formed from a pool of 8 people? | $_8C_5$ which equals 56. |

16. GRAPHS OF TRIG FUNCTIONS

Given a function in the form y = asinbx or y = acosbx, students quiz each other on the amplitude, period, and/or frequency of the graph.

| State the period of the graph $y = \frac{1}{2} \sin 3x$ | period $= \frac{2\pi}{3}$ |

17. ANGLE SUM AND DIFFERENCE FORMULAS

Given an expression such as "Cos45Cos30 - sin45Sin30," students must re-state the expression as a single trig function value.

| Express $\sin 80 \cos 20 - \sin 20 \cos 80$ as the single trig. function of an angle | sin 60 |

18. INVERSE TRIG FUNCTIONS

Given an inverse trig function, such as $\text{ArcSin}(-\frac{1}{2})$, students quiz each other on the value of the given function. Answers may be expressed in degrees or radians, depending on the teachers discretion.

Evaluate $\text{Arctan} = (-\sqrt{3})$	-60^0 or $\dfrac{-\pi}{3}$

B L A C K L I N E   M A S T E R S

Inside-Outside Circle

Algebra 2 and Trigonometry

Trigometric Values of Special Angles
(0°, 30°, 45°, 60°, 90°, 180°, 270°, 360°)

OBJECTIVES

Given a trig function of a special angle (such as sin315 or tan60), students will determine the exact trig function value in fractional/radical form.

MATERIALS

Inside-Outside Circle flashcards (see following pages)

PRE-REQUISITE LEARNING

Students should be able to determine the reference angle for angles greater than 90°. They should also know which trig functions are positive or negative in the various quadrants. Finally, students should know the trig function values for 30°, 45°, 60°, and the quadrantal angles.

FOLLOW-UP ACTIVITY

Once students have mastered sine, cosine, and tangent for the special angles, an Inside-Outside Circle activity can be developed which incorporates secant, cosecant, and cotangent.

Trigonometric Values of Special Angles
(0°, 30°, 45°, 60°, 90°, 270°, 360°)

sin 30	$\dfrac{1}{2}$
sin 0	0
sin 45	$\dfrac{\sqrt{2}}{2}$
sin 120	$\dfrac{\sqrt{3}}{2}$
sin 90	1

Kagan Publishing • 1 (800) 933-2667
www.KaganOnline.com

Cooperative Learning Activities for High School Mathematics
Dina Kushnir

Trigonometric Values of Special Angles
(0°, 30°, 45°, 60°, 90°, 270°, 360°)

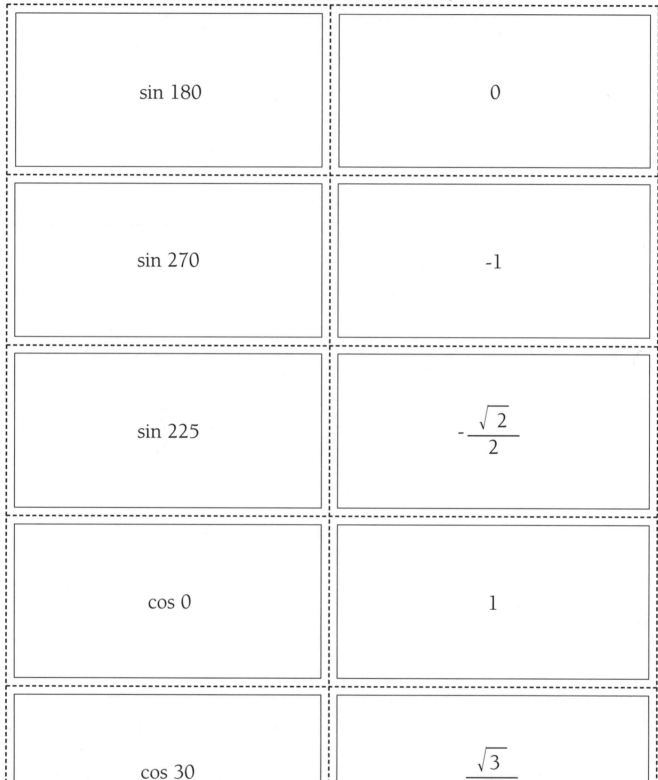

sin 180	0
sin 270	-1
sin 225	$-\dfrac{\sqrt{2}}{2}$
cos 0	1
cos 30	$\dfrac{\sqrt{3}}{2}$

Trigonometric Values of Special Angles
(0°, 30°, 45°, 60°, 90°, 270°, 360°)

cos 135	$-\dfrac{\sqrt{2}}{2}$
cos 60	$\dfrac{1}{2}$
cos 90	0
cos 180	-1
cos 300	1/2

Cooperative Learning Activities for High School Mathematics
Dina Kushnir

Trigonometric Values of Special Angles
(0°, 30°, 45°, 60°, 90°, 270°, 360°)

cos 330	$\dfrac{\sqrt{3}}{2}$
tan 30	$\dfrac{\sqrt{3}}{3}$
tan 45	1
tan 60	$\sqrt{3}$
tan 90	undefined

Trigonometric Values of Special Angles
(0°, 30°, 45°, 60°, 90°, 270°, 360°)

tan 180	0
tan 270	undefined
sin 150	$\dfrac{1}{2}$
sin 210	$\dfrac{-1}{2}$
sin 300	$-\dfrac{\sqrt{3}}{2}$

Cooperative Learning Activities for High School Mathematics
Dina Kushnir

Trigonometric Values of Special Angles
(0°, 30°, 45°, 60°, 90°, 270°, 360°)

cos 210	$-\dfrac{\sqrt{3}}{2}$
cos 120	$\dfrac{-1}{2}$
cos 315	$\dfrac{\sqrt{2}}{2}$
tan 135	-1
tan 300	$-\sqrt{3}$

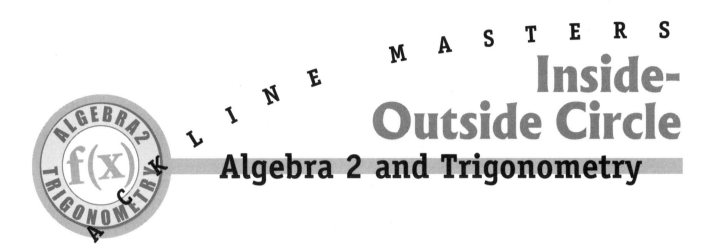

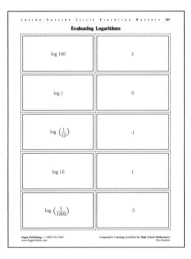

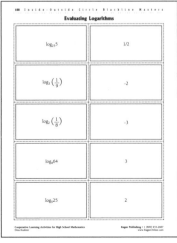

Evaluating Logarithms

OBJECTIVES

Students will evaluate logarithms, such as $\log_3 9$ or log 1000.

MATERIALS

Inside-Outside Circle flashcards (see following pages)

PRE-REQUISITE LEARNING

Students should be familiar with fractional and negative exponents, as well as zero exponents. They should also have a few powers of 2, 3, 4, 5, and 10 memorized. Finally, students should understand that $\log_a b = c$ means that $a^c = b$.

FOLLOW-UP ACTIVITY

Once students are comfortable evaluating logarithms, they may then try solving equations which involve log expressions. For example, $\log_x \frac{1}{3} = -1$ or $\log_2 x = 5$.

Evaluating Logarithms

log 100	2
log 1	0
$\log\left(\dfrac{1}{10}\right)$	-1
log 10	1
$\log\left(\dfrac{1}{1000}\right)$	-3

Evaluating Logarithms

$\log_{25}5$	1/2
$\log_3\left(\dfrac{1}{9}\right)$	-2
$\log_2\left(\dfrac{1}{8}\right)$	-3
$\log_4 64$	3
$\log_5 25$	2

Evaluating Logarithms

$\log_3 9$	2
$\log_3 27$	3
$\log_9 3$	$\dfrac{1}{2}$
$\log_9 81$	2
$\log 1000$	3

Evaluating Logarithms

$\log\left(\dfrac{1}{100}\right)$	-2
$\log_2 8$	3
$\log_2 4$	2
$\log_2\left(\dfrac{1}{2}\right)$	-1
$\log_2 1$	0

Evaluating Logarithms

$\log_2 2$	1
$\log_2\left(\dfrac{1}{4}\right)$	-2
$\log_4 2$	1/2
$\log_4 16$	2
$\log_9\left(\dfrac{1}{9}\right)$	-1

Kagan Publishing • 1 (800) 933-2667
www.KaganOnline.com

Cooperative Learning Activities for High School Mathematics
Dina Kushnir

Evaluating Logarithms

$\log_9\left(\dfrac{1}{3}\right)$	-1/2
$\log_4\left(\dfrac{1}{2}\right)$	$\dfrac{-1}{2}$
$\log_7 1$	0
$\log_{100} 10$	$\dfrac{1}{2}$
$\log_{100}\left(\dfrac{1}{100}\right)$	-1

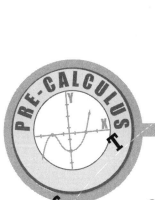

A C T I V I T I E S

Inside-Outside Circle
Pre-Calculus

1. DETERMINANTS

Given a 2 x 2 determinant, students quiz each other on the value of the given determinant.

Evaluate $\begin{bmatrix} 5 & 3 \\ -1 & 0 \end{bmatrix}$	3

2. SERIES AND SEQUENCES

Given a series of three or more numbers, students must determine whether the given series is arithmetic, geometric or neither.

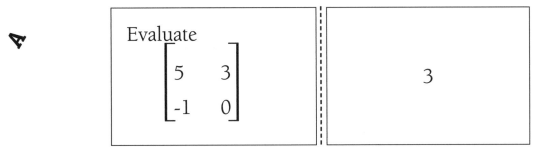

5, 8, 11, 14,...	arithmetic

pgs. 199-204

3. IDENTIFYING CONIC SECTIONS

Given an equation in two variables, students must determine whether the equation is that of a line, parabola, circle, ellipse, or hyperbola.

$5x^2 - 9y^2 = 45$	hyperbola

4. SPECIAL FACTORING TECHNIQUES

Students must factor a given expression. Factoring techniques required include factoring the sum and difference of two cubes and factoring by grouping.

factor $x^3 - 8$	$(x - 2)(x^2 + 2x + 4)$

5. WRITING FUNCTIONS

Given a word problem, students must write a function as indicated in the directions. For example: "Two numbers add to 16. If one of the numbers is x, express the product of the numbers in terms of x."

Two numbers have a product of 50. If one number is x, express the sum of the 2 numbers as a function of x.	$x + \dfrac{50}{x}$

6. Rational Functions

Given a rational function, students quiz each other on the x-intercept(s), the y-intercept, the vertical asymptotes, or the horizontal asymptote.

State the equation of the horizontal asymptote for $$y = \dfrac{(2x + 1)^2\,(x - 5)}{(x + 8)\,(x - 1)^2}$$	$y = 4$

7. Using the Scientific Calculator

Students quiz each other on evaluating various expressions to the nearest 100th. For example, "Sec 173°" or "log 52" or "ArcSin(.3241)."

Evaluate $\cot\left(\dfrac{8\pi}{9}\right)$ to the nearest 100th	-2.75

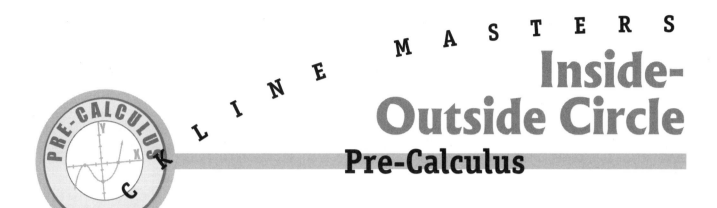

BLACKLINE MASTERS

Inside-Outside Circle

Pre-Calculus

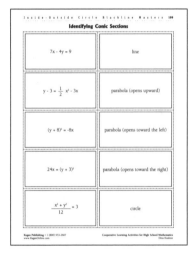

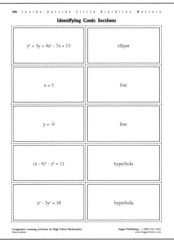

Identifying Conic Sections

OBJECTIVES

Given an equation, students will determine whether the graph of the equation results in a line, circle, parabola, ellipse, or hyperbola

MATERIALS

Inside-Outside Circle flashcards (see following pages)

PRE-REQUISITE LEARNING

Students should be familiar with the standard form equations for lines, circles, ellipses, parabolas, and hyperbolas, as shown on the following page...

LINES	PARABOLAS	CIRCLES
$y = mx+b$	$y = ax^2+bx+c$	$x^2+y^2 = r^2$
$y-y_1 = m(x-x_1)$	$x = ay^2+by+c$	$(x-h)^2+(y-k)^2 = r^2$
	$(y-k)^2 = 4p(x-h)$	$ax^2+ay^2 = k$
	$(x-h)^2 = 4p(y-k)$	$\dfrac{(x-h)^2}{a^2} + \dfrac{(y-k)^2}{a^2} = 1$

ELLIPSES	HYPERBOLAS
$ax^2 + by^2 = c$	$ax^2 - by^2 = k$
$a(x-h)^2+b(y-k)^2 = c$	$ay^2 - bx^2 = k$
$\dfrac{(x-h)^2}{a^2} + \dfrac{(y-k)^2}{b^2} = 1$	$xy = k$
	$\dfrac{(x-h)^2}{a^2} - \dfrac{(y-k)^2}{b^2} = 1$

FOLLOW-UP ACTIVITY

Once students are comfortable identifying and graphing conic sections, they may then begin to graph conics whose equations are in polar form. An Inside-Outside Circle activity may be written in which students are given an equation in polar form and must determine whether it would graph as a parabola, ellipse, circle, or hyperbola.

Identifying Conic Sections

$7x - 4y = 9$	line
$y - 3 = \dfrac{1}{2} x^2 - 3x$	parabola (opens upward)
$(y + 8)^2 = -8x$	parabola (opens toward the left)
$24x = (y + 3)^2$	parabola (opens toward the right)
$\dfrac{x^2 + y^2}{12} = 3$	circle

Identifying Conic Sections

$y^2 + 3y + 4x^2 - 7x = 15$	ellipse
$x = 5$	line
$y = -9$	line
$(x - 6)^2 - y^2 = 12$	hyperbola
$x^2 - 3y^2 = 18$	hyperbola

Identifying Conic Sections

$6y^2 - 2x^2 = 12$	hyperbola
$xy = 6$	hyperbola
$y = \dfrac{8}{x}$	hyperbola
$\dfrac{(x + 3)^2}{5} + \dfrac{(y - 1)^2}{9} = 1$	ellipse
$\dfrac{x^2}{8} + \dfrac{y^2}{8} = 1$	circle

Kagan Publishing • 1 (800) 933-2667
www.KaganOnline.com

Cooperative Learning Activities for High School Mathematics
Dina Kushnir

Identifying Conic Sections

$$\frac{(x-6)^2}{4} + \frac{(y+3)^2}{4} = 1$$	circle
$$\frac{x^2}{49} + \frac{y^2}{16} = 1$$	ellipse
$$\frac{x^2}{5} - y^2 = 1$$	hyperbola
$$\frac{y^2}{10} - \frac{(x+3)^2}{20} = 1$$	hyperbola
$$y = 5x - 6$$	line

Identifying Conic Sections

$y - 6 = \dfrac{2}{5}(x + 7)$	line
$y - 7 = 3x^2 - 2x$	parabola (opens upward)
$x = 6y^2 - 4y + 1$	parabola (opens to the right)
$y^2 = 12x$	parabola (opens to the right)
$(x + 4)^2 = -16y$	parabola (opens downward)

Identifying Conic Sections

$x^2 + y^2 = 25$	circle
$(x - 3)^2 + (y + 1)^2 = 10$	circle
$3x^2 + 3y^2 = 21$	circle
$5x^2 + 3y^2 = 15$	ellipse
$7(x - 3)^2 + 9(y + 4)^2 = 12$	ellipse

RallyCoach

Steps at a Glance

1. The teacher poses a problem to which there is one correct answer.

2. Partner A solves the problem; Partner B watches, checks, and praises.

3. Teacher poses the next problem.

4. Partner B solves the problem; Partner A watches, checks, and praises.

5. Repeat starting at Step 1.

In RallyCoach, students pair up and decide who will be Person A and who will be Person B. There is only one piece of paper and one pencil for each student pair. The teacher poses a problem, either verbally or on paper. Person A begins contributing to the solution of the problem in writing and also states aloud what (s)he is doing (i.e. – "I am using the Pythagorean theorem to find the length of the hypotenuse.") Meanwhile, Person B watches, listens, and coaches. When Person A is done, the paper passes to Person B. Person B writes his/her initials if Person A's work is correct and gives praise. If the work is incorrect, Person B coaches and re-teaches before praising and initialing. Partners now reverse roles, with Person B adding to the solution of the problem and Person A coaching and praising. The paper is passed back and forth between partners until a solution is reached.

RALLYCOACH

Once partners agree on the solution to the given problem, they may either hand their paper in to the teacher or swap papers with another pair of students for checking purposes.

RallyCoach is useful for...

Multi-Step problems (as explained above)

Completing worksheets (Person A does Problem #1, Person B does Problem #2, etc.)

Generating Lists (for example, A and B take turns listing all the palindromes less than 500)

Following is a list of ideas for incorporating RallyCoach into your teaching repertoire.

Several reproducible blackline masters are also provided. Each set of blacklines includes two problem sheets, one in which Person A begins the problem and one in which Person B begins. This way, if you choose to have each pair of students do a particular type of problem, Person A and Person B both get to experience all the different steps necessary for reaching a solution.

The chapter following this one is entitled RoundTable. RoundTable is very similar to RallyCoach but it involves four students instead of two. Many RoundTable activities can be modified and used as RallyCoach activities, and vice versa. Check out the next chapter for more great ideas!

RallyCoach Contents

PRE-ALGEBRA

- Activities 209
- Blackline Masters 215

ALGEBRA 1

- Activities 219
- Blackline Masters 225

GEOMETRY

- Activities 229
- Blackline Masters 233

ALGEBRA 2

- Activities 237
- Blackline Masters 245

TRIGONOMETRY

- Activities 237
- Blackline Masters 255

PRE-CALCULUS

- Activities 259
- Blackline Masters 263

Rally Coach

Management Tips

1 Only one paper and one pencil per pair.

2 You may want to create a record sheet with clearly defined responsibilities for Person A and Person B. See the blackline masters in this chapter for some examples.

3 Model the gambits for coaching and constructive criticism. For example, "I think you made a calculation error here" or "You left out a vital step here." Students may generate a list of gambits before beginning the activity.

4 Explain and model the difference between coaching and giving the answer.

5 Shoulder partners (the person next to you) work better than face partners (the person across from you). It is difficult to check a face partner's paper since it is upside down.

Social Skills

1 Coaching others

2 Patience (giving others time to work)

3 Asking for help

4 Appropriate noise level

5 Offering help

6 Giving and accepting praise

7 Giving and accepting constructive criticism

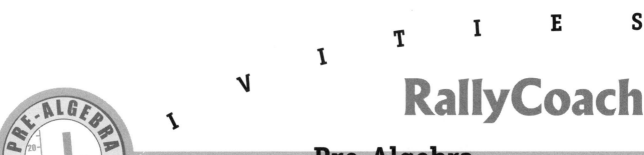

RallyCoach

Pre-Algebra

NOTE

Many more ideas can be found in the chapter on RoundTables. Most RoundTables can be modified to be used as RallyCoaches.

FORMULA SHEETS

While in pairs, each partner adds to a list any formulas needed for the current unit of study (or the final exam). The paper passes back and forth between partners until all pertinent formulas are listed.

> Formulas for this unit...
> △ A = $\frac{1}{2}$bh
>
> ☐ A = l • w
>
> ☐ P = 2l + 2w

1. FACTORS OF A NUMBER

Given a whole number, Person A and Person B take turns writing the given number as the product of two factors. The paper passes back and forth until all possible answers have been written.

> Express 48 as a product of two whole numbers.
>
> Person A : 4 x 12
> Person B : 2 x 24
> Person A : 48 x 1
> Person B : 3 x 16   etc.

2. COMMON FACTORS

Given two or three whole numbers, Person A and Person B take turns writing down a common factor of the given numbers. The paper passes back and forth until all common factors are listed. To close the activity, the partners may be asked to state the greatest common factor of the numbers.

Find all the common factors of 24, 48, and 36.

Person A	Person B
2	1
3	12
6	4
	etc.

3. ONE-STEP EQUATIONS

Students are given a "target number," such as 8. Partners take turns writing a one-step equation whose solution is the target number. The paper passes back and forth until 6 to 8 equations are listed, or until every operation has been used at least once.

Write an equation whose solution is 7.

Person A	Person B
$x + 5 = 12$	$3x = 21$
$\frac{x}{2} = 3.5$	$15 - x = 8$
	etc.

4. Operations on Integers

Given two integers, a and b...

Person A: Computes a + b

Person B: Computes a - b

Person A: Computes ab

Person B: Computes a/b (Round to the nearest 10th if necessary)

This activity can also be done with *fractions, decimals,* or *monomials.*

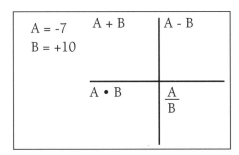

5. Equivalent Decimals, Fractions, and Percents

Partners are given a shaded diagram, such as the one below...

Person A: Writes a fraction to express the shaded region

Person B: Writes a decimal to express the shaded region

Person A: Writes a percent to express the shaded region

Person B: Writes a fraction, decimal, or percent to express the unshaded region.

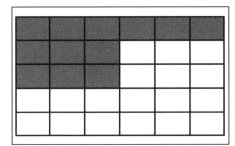

Express the <u>shaded</u> region as a...
A ... Fraction
B ... Decimal
A ... Percent
B ... Express the <u>unshaded</u> region
as a decimal

6. INTERPRETING GRAPHS

Partners are given a graph or other data display. Students pass the paper back and forth as they take turns answering various questions about the data. For example, "Who sold the most cars?" or "During which span of years was the population decreasing?", etc.

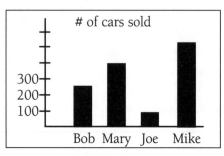

A. Mary sold how many more cars than Bob?

B. What was the total number of cars sold?
etc.

7. PROBLEM SOLVING WITH DECIMALS, FRACTIONS, AND PERCENTS

pgs. 217-218

Students are given a problem solving scenario and take turns contributing to the solution of the problem. For example... "Clothing Mart sell golf shirts for $15.75 each and shorts for $11.00."

Person A: If golf shirts are on sale for 1/3 off, what is the sale price for each shirt?

Person B: If Joe buys 3 golf shirts on sale and 2 pair of shorts, what is the subtotal of this merchandise?

Person A: If sales tax is 7%, what is the sales tax?

Person B: Compute the total purchase price after sales tax. How much change would Joe get if he paid with a $100 bill?

8. MEASUREMENT, SURFACE AREA, AND VOLUME

Students are given an unopened soup can (or other type of can) and a tape measure.

Person A: Measures the height of the can to the nearest tenth of a centimeter.

Person B: Measures the circumference of the can to the nearest tenth of a centimeter.

Person A: Uses the circumference to compute the radius to the nearest tenth of a centimeter

Person B: Finds the lateral surface area to the nearest tenth of a square centimeter.

Person A: Finds the total surface area to the nearest tenth of a square centimeter.

Person B: Finds the volume of the can to the nearest tenth of a cubic centimeter.

9. ORDER OF OPERATIONS

Students are given a target number, such as 10. Partners take turns writing a number sentence involving several operations whose value is the target number. Students evaluate each other's work before adding another number sentence to the list.

Target Number : 10	
Person A	Person B
$6 + 2 \cdot 2$	$5(8 - 6)$
$\dfrac{20}{3 - 1}$	$5^2 - 15$

10. PROPERTIES OF NUMBERS

Students take turns adding to a list of numbers that meet conditions given by the teacher. For example, "List all the prime numbers less than 50," or "List all the multiples of 3 between 20 and 40."

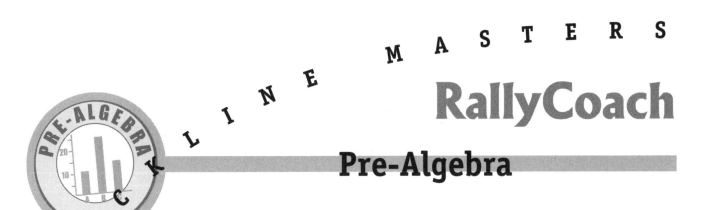

Problem Solving with Percents, Decimals, and Fractions

OBJECTIVES

Students will compute a percent increase or decrease, compute sales tax, multiply, add, and subtract decimals, and determine a fractional part of a number.

MATERIALS

RallyCoach worksheets, pencils, calculators

PREREQUISITE LEARNING

Students should be able to determine a percent of a number, a fraction of a number, and perform operations with decimals.

Kagan Publishing • 1 (800) 933-2667
www.KaganOnline.com

Cooperative Learning Activities for High School Mathematics
Dina Kushnir

FOLLOW-UP ACTIVITY

Once students are comfortable with computing percent discounts and increases, they may advance to problems which require them to work backwards. For example, "If a shirt was priced at $15 last year, and it now costs $22, find the percent of increase."

Problem Solving with Percents, Decimals, and Fractions

Names:

_____

_____

> *Last year, Mark's Fish Stand sold salmon for $6.30/lb. and haddock for $8.40/lb*

Person A: This year, the price of haddock has gone up 20%. Now what is the price of a pound of haddock at Mark's Fish Stand? Show all work, except for calculations done on the calculator.

Person B check and initial:_____

Person B: Janice has a coupon for 1/3 off a pound of salmon. What is the price of a pound of salmon with this coupon? Show all work, except for calculations done on the calculator.

Person A check and initial:_____

Person A: If Janice buys one pound of salmon and 2.4 pounds of haddock, what is the subtotal of her purchase? Show all work, except for calculations done on the calculator.

Person B check and initial:_____

Person B: If sales tax is 5%, what is the final total of Janice's purchase?

Person A check and initial:_____

Problem Solving with Percents, Decimals, and Fractions

Names:

_____

_____

> *Last week, the price of a pair of jeans at Sally's boutique was $45. This week the price has been lowered to $27. A t-shirt costs $8.35.*

Person A: What is the percent decrease in price on a pair of jeans? Show all work, except for calculations done on the calculator.

Person B check and initial:_____

Person B: What is the retail price if Jake buys 2 pair of jeans and three t-shirts? Show all work, except for calculations done on the calculator.

Person A check and initial:_____

Person A: Jake has a coupon for 15% off his total purchase. What is his subtotal after the coupon discount is applied? Show all work, except for calculations done on the calculator.

Person B check and initial:_____

Person B: If there is no sales tax, how much change will Jake receive if he pays with a $100 bill? Show all work, except for calculations done on the calculator.

Person A check and initial:_____

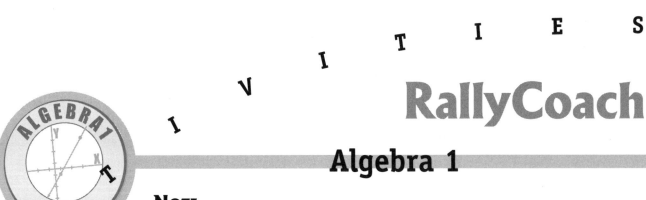

RallyCoach

Algebra 1

NOTE

Many more ideas can be found in the chapter on RoundTables. Most RoundTables can be modified to be used as RallyCoaches.

FORMULA SHEETS

While in pairs, each partner adds to a list any formulas needed for the current unit of study (or the final exam). The paper passes back and forth between partners until all pertinent formulas are listed.

> Formulas for this unit...
>
> $\triangle$ A = $\frac{1}{2}$bh
>
> $\square$ A = l • w
>
> $\square$ P = 2l + 2w

1. WRITING ALGEBRAIC EXPRESSIONS

Students take turns writing algebraic expressions as posed by the teacher, or as written on a worksheet. For example...

Person A: Write "the sum of 12 and a number, P" as an algebraic expression.

Person B: Write "twice the sum of 12 and a number, P" as an algebraic expression.

Person A: Write "half the sum of 12 and a number, P" as an algebraic expression.

Person B: Write "the square of the sum of 12 and a number, P" as an algebraic expression.

> Express in algebraic form...
>
> Person A. The sum of 5 and Q
>
> Person B. The product of 5 and the square of Q.
> etc.

2. EVALUATING ALGEBRAIC EXPRESSIONS

Students write an algebraic expression, and then take turns evaluating the expression for various numbers. For example...

Person A: Write "twice x decreased by half of y" as an algebraic expression.

Person B: Evaluate the expression written by Person A for x = 3 and y = - 8

Person B: Write "half the difference of m and 7" as an algebraic expression

Person A: Evaluate the expression written by Person B for m = 15

> Person A: Write "x more than twice y" as an algebraic expression
>
> Person B: Evaluate the expression above for x=5 and y=-3

Cooperative Learning Activities for High School Mathematics
Dina Kushnir

Kagan Publishing • 1 (800) 933-2667
www.KaganOnline.com

3. SOLVING MULTI-STEP LINEAR EQUATIONS

Students are given a multi-step equation, such as $5(x - 3) = 6 + 2x$. Partners take turns adding just one step toward the solution of the problem. The paper passes back and forth until the solution has been determined and checked.

This activity can be modified to include word problems in one variable, solving and graphing inequalities in one variable, or quadratic equations.

$$5x - 7 = 3(x + 1)$$

4. WRITING MULTI-STEP EQUATIONS

Students are given a target number, such as - 5. Partners take turns writing equations whose solution is the target number. Each equation written must require at least two steps in its solution. Partners can check each other's equations before adding more equations to the list. The paper is passed back and forth until 4 equations are written.

Target number: -8

Person A	Person B
$3x + 5 = -19$	$\frac{x}{2} + 7 = 3$
$2(x - 3) = -22$	$x + 4 = -2x - 20$

5. OPERATIONS ON RADICALS

Given two radical expressions, a and b such as $5\sqrt{2}$ and $2\sqrt{8}$

Person A: Expresses a + b in simplest radical form

Person B: Expresses ab in simplest radical form

Person A: Expresses a^2 in simplest form

Person B: Finds the length of the hypotenuse of a triangle whose legs are a and b, and expresses the result in simplest radical form.

$a = 3\sqrt{8}$	$b = \sqrt{18}$
Express in simplest radical form...	
A. a + b	B. a • b
A. a^2	B. Find x...

6. GRAPHING LINEAR FUNCTIONS

Given a linear equation, such as 3y + 2x = 12...

Person A: Determines two points that lie on the graph of the given equation

Person B: Determines two more points that lie on the graph of the equation

Person A: Graphs the line and determines the y-intercept

Person B: Determines the slope of the line as a fraction in lowest terms.

$$3x + 2y = 12$$

7. ALGEBRA WORD PROBLEMS IN ONE VARIABLE

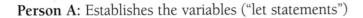

Given an algebra word problem, such as ...

"The length of a rectangle is 5 inches more than the width. If the perimeter is 66 inches, find the dimensions of the rectangle."

Person A: Establishes the variables ("let statements")

Person B: Writes the equation needed to solve the problem

Person A: Solves the equation

Person B: Refers back to the "let statements" and states the final solution to the problem.

The types of word problems used in this activity can include consecutive integer problems, motion problems, money problems, age problems, percentage problems, mixture problems, area problems, etc.

> The sum of 3 consecutive odd integers is 27.
> A. "Let" statements
> B. Write an equation
> A. Solve the equation
> B. State the 3 consecutive odd integers.

8. Writing, Evaluating, Transforming Formulas

Person A: Write a formula for the number of students, N, who may sit in an auditorium in which there are S single seats and T double seats.

Person B: Solve the above formula for S

Person A: Refer back to the original formula and solve this for T

Person B: Find the value of S if T = 50 and N = 325.

pgs. 226-227

A video store charges $2 to rent a video for 3 days, then $.50 for each additional day. Write a formula to represent the cost, c, of keeping a video for x days.

9. The Real Number System

Students take turns listing numbers that meet given criteria.

Person A: Find a real number that is not a whole number

Person B: Find an integer that is also a natural number

Person A: Find a rational number that is not an integer

Person B: Find a real number that is not rational

The possibilities for these types of prompts are endless

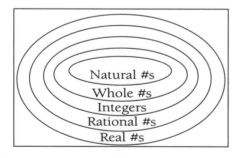

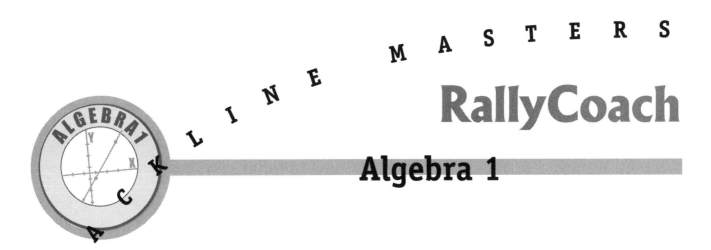

RallyCoach

Algebra 1

Writing, Evaluating, and Transforming Formulas

OBJECTIVES

Students will write a formula based on a given verbal problem. They will also solve this formula for one variable in terms of the others. Finally, students will evaluate a formula for given variable values.

MATERIALS

RallyCoach worksheets, pencils

PREREQUISITE LEARNING

Students should be able to write algebraic phrases based on given verbal phrases. Students should be able to use substitution to evaluate an algebraic expression and also be able to solve linear equations.

Writing, Evaluating, and Transforming Formulas

Names:

_____

_____

> *A long distance telephone call costs x cents for the first 3 minutes and y cents for each additional minute.*

Person A: Write a formula for the cost, C, of a telephone call lasting 9 minutes.

Person B check and initial:_____

Person B: Solve the above formula for y.

Person A check and initial:_____

Person A: Suppose you make a 15 minute phone call. Now what is the new formula for C?

Person B check and initial:_____

Person B: If C = 95 cents and y = 4, find the value of x for a 15 minute phone call.

Person A check and initial:_____

Writing, Evaluating, and Transforming Formulas

Names:

_____

_____

> **In a certain lounge, there are C chairs and L love seats. Each chair seats one person and each love seat seats 2 people.**

Person A: Write a formula for S, the total number of seats in the lounge.

Person B check and initial:_____

Person B: Solve the above formula for L.

Person A check and initial:_____

Person A: Solve the original formula for C

Person B check and initial:_____

Person B: If S = 210 and C = 38, find the value of L.

Person A check and initial:_____

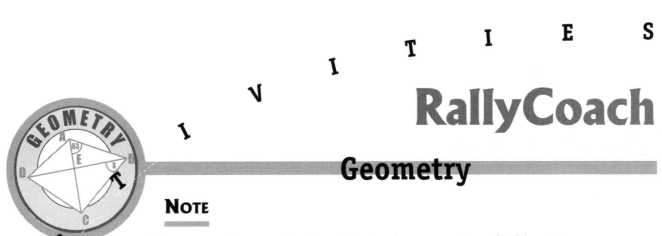

RallyCoach
Geometry

Note

Many more ideas can be found in the chapter on RoundTables. Most RoundTables can be modified to be used as RallyCoaches.

Formula Sheets

While in pairs, each partner adds to a list any formulas needed for the current unit of study (or the final exam). The paper passes back and forth between partners until all pertinent formulas are listed.

> Formulas for this unit...
>
> $\triangle A = \dfrac{1}{2}bh$
>
> $\square A = l \cdot w$
>
> $\square P = 2l + 2w$

1. CONSTRUCTIONS

Each pair gets one compass and one straightedge. At the top of a piece of paper is a scalene triangle labeled △ABC.

Person A: Constructs a median to side $\overline{AC}$

Person B: Constructs an altitude to side $\overline{BC}$

Person A: Constructs an isosceles triangle whose legs are congruent to $\overline{AC}$ and whose base is congruent to $\overline{AB}$. Label this new triangle △DEF

Person B: Constructs the bisector of ∠BCA

pgs. 234-235

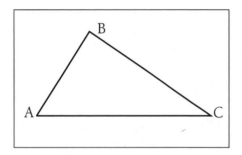

2. GEOMETRY PROOFS

Each pair is given a geometry proof with some given information and a diagram. Partners take turns adding two steps (statement and reason) to the proof, passing the paper back and forth until the proof is completed.

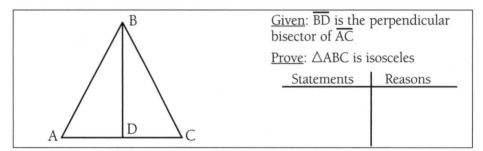

Given: $\overline{BD}$ is the perpendicular bisector of $\overline{AC}$

Prove: △ABC is isosceles

Statements	Reasons

3. GEOMETRY PROBLEM SOLVING

Students are given a geometric diagram, such as the one shown below. Partners take turns finding various angle measures and/or segment lengths in the diagram.

Person A: Find the value of x.

Person B: Find the lengths of $\overline{AD}, \overline{AB}, \overline{BC}$

Person A: What type of parallelogram is ABCD?

Person B: Find m $\angle$ACB

Person A: Find m $\angle$BDC

Person B: Find m $\angle$DAB

The diagrams given to students for these types of problems may include parallel lines, isosceles triangles, all types of quadrilaterals, circles, chords, secants, tangents, special right triangles, similar triangles, etc.

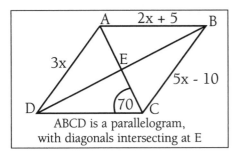

ABCD is a parallelogram,
with diagonals intersecting at E

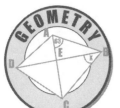

4. PROPERTIES OF QUADRILATERALS

The teacher states a property, such as "Congruent diagonals." Person A writes that property at the top of the paper and then partners take turns writing down a type of quadrilateral the has that property. The paper passes back and forth until all the appropriate quadrilaterals are listed. The teacher then states another property, such as "At least one pair of opposite sides are parallel." Partners again pass the paper back and forth as they develop a list of appropriate quadrilaterals. This process can be repeated as many times as the teacher sees fit.

Property:	
"Opposite angles congruent"	
Person A	Person B
Parallelogram	Rectangle
Square	Rhombus

5. CORRESPONDING PARTS OF CONGRUENT TRIANGLES

Students are given a drawing of two triangles, with several parts marked congruent or some information given. An example is shown below. Partners must agree on which postulate would be used to prove the triangles congruent (AAS, SSS, ASA, SAS, or HL). Partners then take turns listing pairs of congruent corresponding parts between the two triangles.

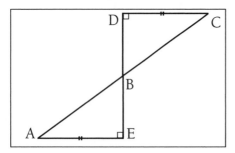

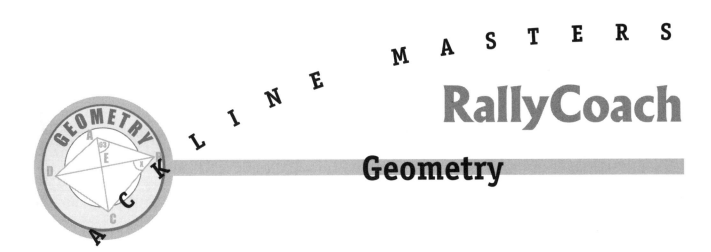

Constructions

OBJECTIVES

Students will construct angle bisectors, perpendicular lines, parallel lines, triangles, medians, and segment bisectors

MATERIALS

RallyCoach worksheets, pencils, compasses, straight edges

PREREQUISITE LEARNING

Students should be able to use a compass and straightedge to find midpoints, and to construct angle bisectors, perpendicular and parallel lines, congruent segments and congruent angles.

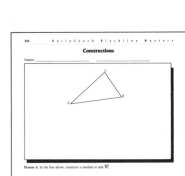

Constructions

Names: _____   _____

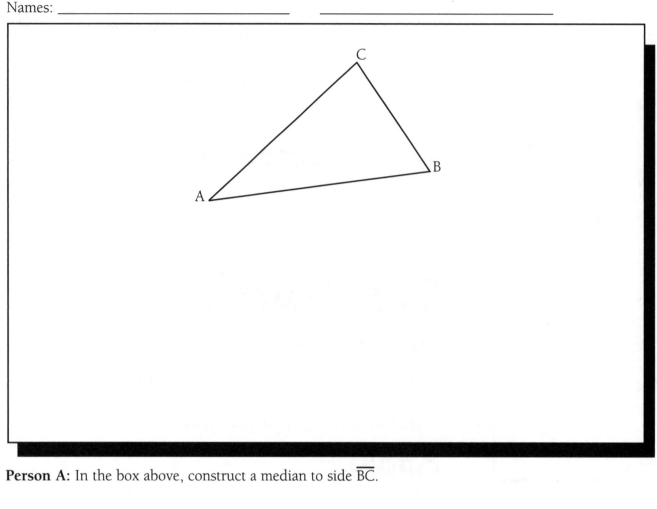

Person A: In the box above, construct a median to side $\overline{BC}$.

Person B check and initial:_____

Person B: Construct an altitude to $\overline{AB}$.

Person A check and initial:_____

Person A: Construct an isosceles triangle with legs congruent to $\overline{BC}$ and base congruent to $\overline{AC}$. Label the new triangle $\triangle DEF$

Person B check and initial:_____

Person B: Bisect the vertex angle of $\triangle DEF$.

Person A check and initial:_____

Constructions

Names: _____   _____

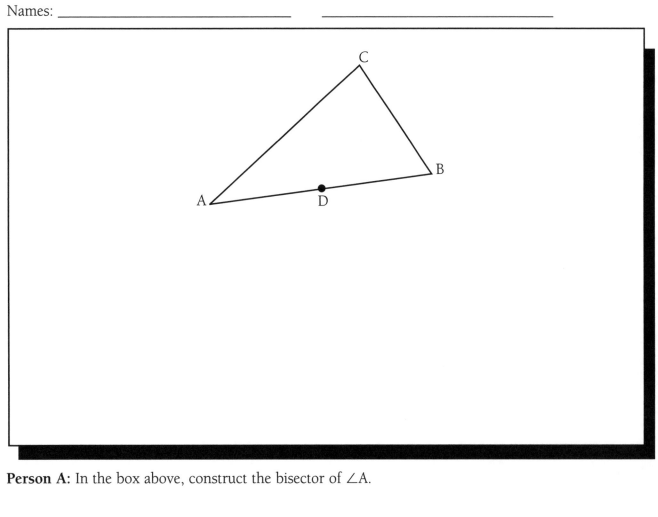

Person A: In the box above, construct the bisector of ∠A.

Person A check and initial:_____

Person B: Construct a line perpendicular to $\overline{AB}$ and passing through D.

Person B check and initial:_____

Person A: Construct a triangle congruent to △ABC. Label the new triangle △DEF

Person A check and initial:_____

Person B: Construct a line parallel to $\overline{DE}$ and passing through F.

Person B check and initial:_____

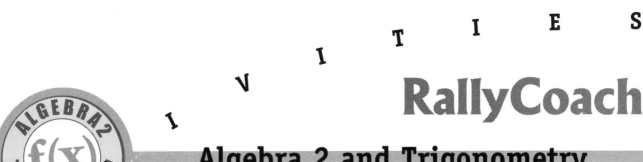

RallyCoach
Algebra 2 and Trigonometry

NOTE

Many more ideas can be found in the chapter on RoundTables. Most RoundTables can be modified to be used as RallyCoaches.

FORMULA SHEETS

While in pairs, each partner adds to a list any formulas needed for the current unit of study (or the final exam). The paper passes back and forth between partners until all pertinent formulas are listed.

> Formulas for this unit...
> $\triangle \ A = \dfrac{1}{2}bh$
> $\square \ A = 1 \cdot w$
> $\square \ P = 21 + 2w$

1. COORDINATE GEOMETRY PROOFS

Given the points A(1, 4), B(3, 5), C(7, 2), D(5, 1). Plot Quadrilateral ABCD on a piece of graph paper. Using the distance, midpoint, and slope formulas...

Person A: Prove whether or not the diagonals bisect each other.

Person B: Prove whether or not $\overline{AB}$ is parallel to $\overline{CD}$. Is ABCD a parallelogram? Why or why not?

Person A: Prove whether of not $\overline{AB} \cong \overline{BC}$. Is ABCD a rhombus? Why or why not?

Person B: Prove whether or not $\angle BCD$ is a right angle. Is ABCD a rectangle?

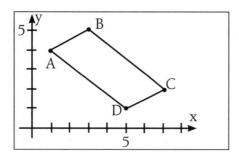

2. LAWS OF SINES AND COSINES, AREA OF A TRIANGLE

Given a geometric diagram, such as the one given below...

Person A: Find SQ to the nearest 10th.

Person B: Find $\angle PQS$ to the nearest degree.

Person A: Find SP to the nearest 10th.

Person B: Find the area of $\triangle PSR$ to the nearest 10th of a square unit.

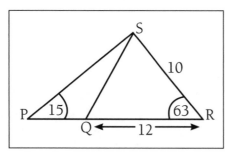

3. Right Triangle Trigonometry

Students are given a labeled diagram involving right triangles. Using right triangle trigonometry, students take turns finding various angle measures and segment lengths.

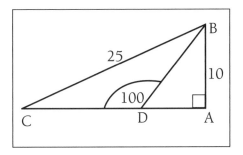

pgs. 256-257

4. Function Graphs (Compositions and Inverses)

Students are given the graphs of f(x) and g(x). An example is shown below...

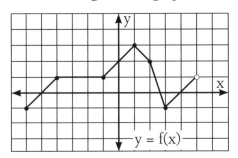 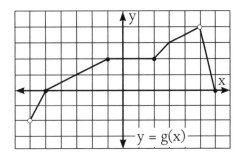

Person A: Evaluate f(g(2))

Person B: Evaluate g(f(- 1))

Person A: Sketch the graph of $f^{-1}(x)$

Person B: Determine $f^{-1}(3)$

Person A: If g(a) = 0, find all possible values of a

Person B: Is $g^{-1}(x)$ a function? Why or why not?

5. LINEAR EQUATIONS IN TWO VARIABLES

Students take turns solving problems dealing with the equation of a line.

For example...

Person A: Find k if the point (3, -2) lies on the graph of 2x + ky = 12

Person B: Using the answer for k above determine the slope and y-intercept of 2x + ky = 12.

Person A: Write the equation of a line parallel to 2x + ky = 12 and passing through (-3, 9)

Person B: Find the slope of a line that would be perpendicular to the line 2x + ky = 12.

> (3, -2) lies on the
> graph of
> 2x + ky = 12

6. SOLVING SYSTEMS OF EQUATIONS BY GRAPHING

Given the equations of two conic sections...

Person A: Graphs the first equation

Person B: Graphs the second equation

Person A: States the solution(s) to the system of equations

Person B: Checks the solutions

The above activity can be modified to include graphing systems of inequalities in two variables.

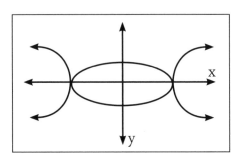

pgs. 247-249

7. GRAPHING CONIC SECTIONS

Given the equation of an ellipse...

Person 1 - Writes the equation in standard form

Person 2 - Finds the coordinates of the center and the endpoints of the major axis

Person 1 - Finds the coordinates of the endpoints of the minor axis

Person 2 - Finds the coordinates of the foci and sketches a graph

Note: This activity can be modified to include graphs of parabolas or hyperbolas.

$$5(x - 2)^2 + 9(y + 3)^2 = 45$$

$$8x^2 + 32x + 2y^2 - 4y = 10$$

8. Graphing Linear Equations in Three Variables

Given the plane $2x + 2y + 3z = 12$...

Person A: Determine the x- and y-intercepts of the plane

Person B: Determine the z-intercept. Does $(1, -2, 3)$ lie in the plane?

Person A: Tell whether or not the graph is parallel to or contains any of the coordinate axes. If so, which ones?

Person B: Tell whether or not the graph is parallel to or coincides with one of the coordinate planes. If so, which one?

This activity can be repeated for the plane $x = 3$.

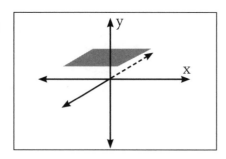

9. Trigonometric Graphs

Given the equations of two trig graphs, such as $y = -2\sin x$ and $y = \cos 2x$...

Person A: Graphs the first equation for $0 \leqslant x \leqslant 2\pi$

Person B: Graphs the second equation for $0 \leqslant x \leqslant 2\pi$

Person A: How many values of x in the interval $0 \leqslant x \leqslant 2\pi$ satisfy the equation $-2\sin x = \cos 2x$?

Person B: What value of x in $0 \leqslant x \leqslant 2\pi$ satisfies the equation $(-2\sin x) - (\cos 2x) = 3$?

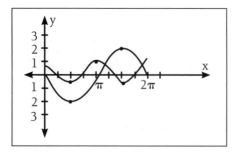

10. MEASURES OF CENTRAL TENDENCY

Given a set of grouped data, students take turns finding various measures of central tendency, including the mean, median, mode, mean absolute deviation, and standard deviation.

x_i	f_i
10	1
15	3
20	2
25	4

pgs. 252-254

11. SOLVING QUADRATIC EQUATIONS

Students are given two quadratic equations, such as $3x^2 + 9x = 1$ and $4x^2 = 3(x + 2)$

Person A: Completes the square for the first equation.

Person B: Solves the first equation.

Person B: Gets the second equation into standard form, $ax^2 + bx + c = 0$

Person A: Solves the second equation using the quadratic formula or by factoring.

> Solve by completing
> the square...
>
> $3x^2 + 9x = 1$

Cooperative Learning Activities for High School Mathematics
Dina Kushnir

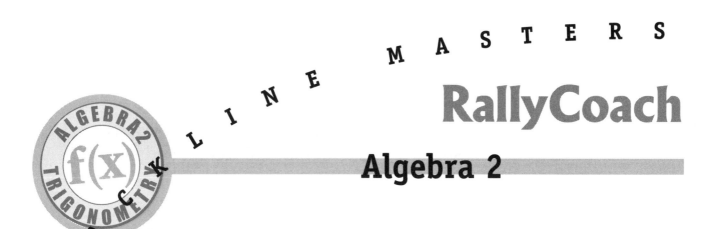

Solving Systems of Equations by Graphing

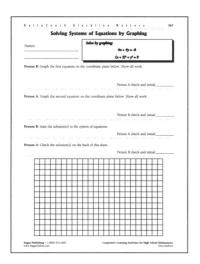

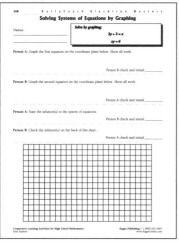

OBJECTIVES

Students will solve a linear - quadratic system of equations in two variables by graphing.

MATERIALS

RallyCoach worksheets, pencils

PREREQUISITE LEARNING

Students should be able to graph a line, circle, and hyperbola in the form $xy = k$.

FOLLOW-UP ACTIVITY

Once students are comfortable with graphing systems involving lines, circles, and hyperbolas in the form $xy = k$, more types of equations can be added to this activity. You may choose to include parabolas, ellipses, transformed ellipses, hyperbolas in the form $ax^2 - by^2 = k$ and transformed hyperbolas.

Another possible follow - up activity is to graph systems of inequalities in two variables, where students shade in the solution set and label it "S."

Solving Systems of Equations by Graphing

Names:

_____

_____

> ### Solve by graphing:
>
> $$4x + 4y = -8$$
>
> $$(x + 5)^2 + y^2 = 9$$

Person B: Graph the first equation on the coordinate plane below. Show all work.

Person A check and initial:_____

Person A: Graph the second equation on the coordinate plane below. Show all work.

Person B check and initial:_____

Person B: State the solution(s) to the system of equations.

Person A check and initial:_____

Person A: Check the solution(s) on the back of this sheet.

Person B check and initial:_____

Cooperative Learning Activities for High School Mathematics
Dina Kushnir

Solving Systems of Equations by Graphing

Names:

_____

_____

Solve by graphing:

$$3y + 3 = x$$

$$xy = 6$$

Person A: Graph the first equation on the coordinate plane below. Show all work.

Person B check and initial:_____

Person B: Graph the second equation on the coordinate plane below. Show all work.

Person A check and initial:_____

Person A: State the solution(s) to the system of equations.

Person B check and initial:_____

Person B: Check the solution(s) on the back of this sheet.

Person A check and initial:_____

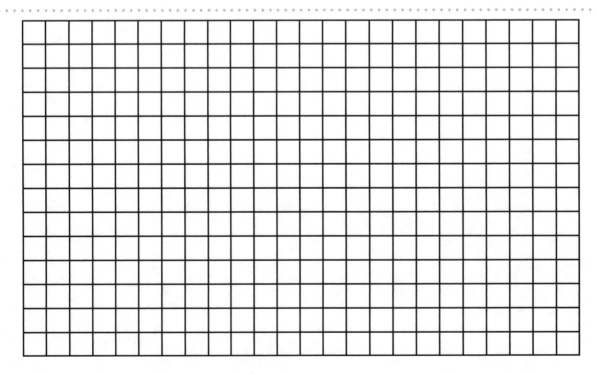

Solving Systems of Equations by Graphing

Names:

_____

_____

Solve by graphing:

Person B: Graph the first equation on the coordinate plane below. Show all work.

Person A check and initial:_____

Person A: Graph the second equation on the coordinate plane below. Show all work.

Person B check and initial:_____

Person B: State the solution(s) to the system of equations.

Person A check and initial:_____

Person A: Check the solution(s) on the back of this sheet.

Person B check and initial:_____

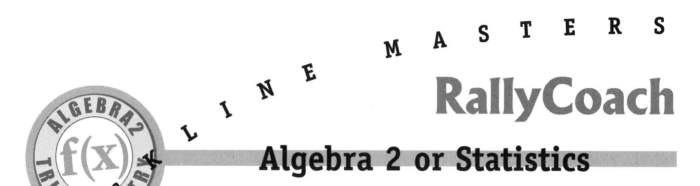

Statistics

OBJECTIVES

Students will determine the mean, median, mode, mean absolute deviation, and standard deviation of a set of grouped data.

MATERIALS

RallyCoach worksheets, pencils, calculators

PREREQUISITE LEARNING

Students should be able to determine the mean, median, mode, mean absolute deviation, and standard deviation of a set of grouped data.

FOLLOW-UP ACTIVITY

Once students have mastered standard deviation, they can start learning about the normal curve (also known as the "bell curve"). RallyTable activities can be developed which ask such questions as... "How many students scored in the 97th percentile?" or "What score represents two standard deviations below the mean?"

Statistics

Names: _____   _____

x_i	f_i
75	3
80	4
85	7
90	5
95	1

Person A: Compute the median and the mode score.

Person B check and initial:_____

Person B: Compute the mean. Round to the nearest 10th if necessary.

Person A check and initial:_____

Person A: Using the answer(s) above, compute the mean absolute deviation to the nearest 10th.

Person B check and initial:_____

Person B: Using the mean computed above, compute the standard deviation to the nearest 10th.

Person A check and initial:_____

Statistics

Names: _____   _____

x_i	f_i
16	4
17	1
18	5
19	2
20	8

Person B: Compute the median and the mode score.

Person A check and initial:_____

Person A: Compute the mean. Round to the nearest 10th if necessary.

Person B check and initial:_____

Person B: Using the answer(s) above, compute the mean absolute deviation to the nearest 10th.

Person A check and initial:_____

Person A: Using the mean computed above, compute the standard deviation to the nearest 10th.

Person B check and initial:_____

Statistics

Names: _____　　_____

x_i	f_i	

Person B: Compute the median and the mode score.

Person A check and initial:_____

Person A: Compute the mean. Round to the nearest 10th if necessary.

Person B check and initial:_____

Person B: Using the answer(s) above, compute the mean absolute deviation to the nearest 10th.

Person A check and initial:_____

Person A: Using the mean computed above, compute the standard deviation to the nearest 10th.

Person B check and initial:_____

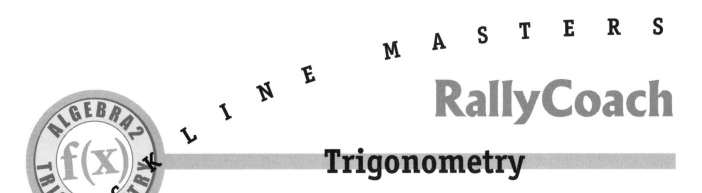

MASTERS
RallyCoach
Trigonometry

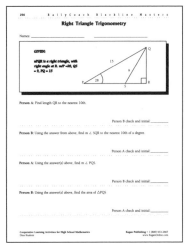

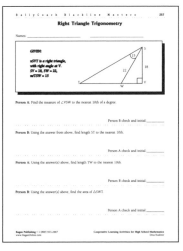

Right Triangle Trigonometry

OBJECTIVES

Students will use sine, cosine, and tangent to determine angle measures and segment lengths.

MATERIALS

RallyCoach worksheets, pencils, scientific calculators

PREREQUISITE LEARNING

Students should be able to determine an angle measure or segment length in a right triangle using sine, cosine, or tangent.

Right Triangle Trigonometry

Names: _____   _____

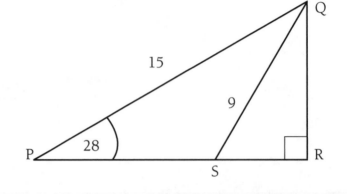

GIVEN:

△*PQR is a right triangle,*
with right angle at R.
m∠P = 28, QS = 9, PQ = 15

Person A: Find length QR to the nearest 10th.

Person B check and initial:_____

Person B: Using the answer from above, find m ∠SQR to the nearest 10th of a degree.

Person A check and initial:_____

Person A: Using the answer(s) above, find m ∠PQS.

Person B check and initial:_____

Person B: Using the answer(s) above, find the area of △PQS.

Person A check and initial:_____

Right Triangle Trigonometry

Names: _____   _____

GIVEN:

$\triangle SVT$ *is a right triangle,*
with right angle at V.
SV = 18, SW = 22,
m∠TSW = 15

Person A: Find the measure of ∠VSW to the nearest 10th of a degree.

Person B check and initial:_____

Person B: Using the answer from above, find length ST to the nearest 10th.

Person A check and initial:_____

Person A: Using the answer(s) above, find length TW to the nearest 10th.

Person B check and initial:_____

Person B: Using the answer(s) above, find the area of △SWT.

Person A check and initial:_____

RallyCoach

Pre-Calculus

NOTE

Many more ideas can be found in the chapter on RoundTables. Most RoundTables can be modified to be used as RallyCoaches.

FORMULA SHEETS

While in pairs, each partner adds to a list any formulas needed for the current unit of study (or the final exam). The paper passes back and forth between partners until all pertinent formulas are listed.

Formulas for this unit...

$$d=\sqrt{(x_1-x_2)^2 + (y_1-y_2)^2}$$

$$\text{parabola:} (y-k)^2 = 4p(x-h)$$

$$\text{ellipse:} \frac{(x-h)^2}{a^2} + \frac{(y-k)^2}{b^2} =1$$

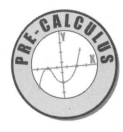

1. GRAPHING INTERVAL FUNCTIONS

Given an interval function, such as...

$$f(x) = \begin{cases} 2x + 6, \ x < -5 & \text{(Person A)} \\ x^2 - 15, \ -5 \le x \le -2 & \text{(Person B)} \\ 3, \ -2 < x < 2 & \text{(Person A)} \\ x^2, \ x \ge 2 & \text{(Person B)} \end{cases}$$

Partners take turns graphing portions of the function.

$$f(x) = \begin{cases} -3x - 5, \ -3 \le x < -1 \\ x^2 + 3, \ -1 \le x \le 1 \\ |x - 5|, \ 1 < x < 6 \\ \sqrt{x + 3}, \ x \ge 6 \end{cases}$$

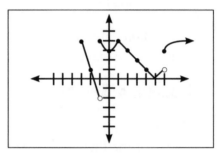

2. GEOMETRIC PROGRESSIONS

Given the progression 12, 6, 3,...

Person A: Finds the value of "r," the common ratio

Person B: Determines the 15th term in the series

Person A: Determines the sum of the infinite series 12, 6, 3,...

Person B: Determines the sum of the first 10 terms in the series

Given the geometric progression
12, 6, 3,...
A. $r =$
B. The 15th term is...
A. $S \infty =$
B. $S_{10} =$

3. LINEAR PROGRAMMING

Given a linear programming word problem...

Person A: Establishes the variables ("let statements") and lists the constraints

Person B: Writes the objective function

Person A: Graphs two of the constraints

Person B: Graphs the remaining constraints

Person A: Lists the critical points

Person B: Determines the final solution.

pgs. 264-265

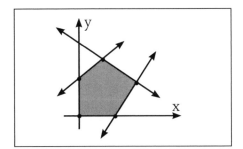

4. POLAR COORDINATES AND DEMOIVRE'S THEOREM

Students are given a complex number, such as 4 - 3i.

Person A: Converts the number to polar form (r, θ), rounding r and θ to the nearest tenth.

Person B: Uses the answer above to find $(4 - 3i)^4$, expressing the answer in polar form (rounding to the nearest tenth).

Person A: Uses DeMoivre's theorem to find one root of $\sqrt[3]{4-3i}$ in polar form (rounding to the nearest tenth).

Person B: Finds the other two roots of $\sqrt[3]{4-3i}$ in polar form (rounding to the nearest tenth).

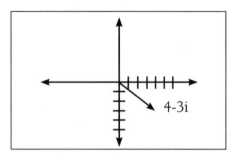

For many other **RallyCoach** ideas, see the chapter on **RoundTables**.

Most **RoundTables** can be modified to become **RallyCoaches**.

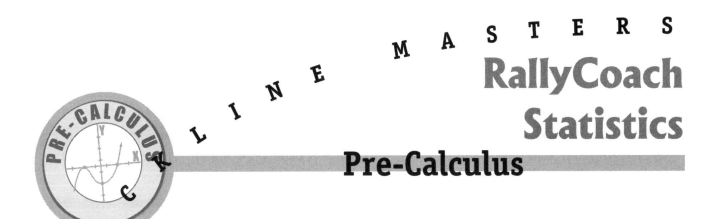

M A S T E R S
RallyCoach
Statistics
Pre-Calculus

Linear Programming

OBJECTIVES

Students will use linear programming to minimize costs and maximize profits

MATERIALS

RallyCoach worksheets, pencils, calculators, graph paper

PREREQUISITE LEARNING

Students should be able to write algebraic equations based on verbal problems, graph linear inequalities, and evaluate algebraic expressions using substitution.

FOLLOW-UP ACTIVITY

Once students have mastered linear programming, they can begin to explore other types of inequality graphs which might involve conic sections, logarithmic functions, or exponential functions.

Linear Programming

Names: _____   _____

> *The Fast - Gro Fertilizer Company guarantees that each bag of fertilizer contains at least 60 lbs. of phosphoric acid and at least 30 lbs. of potash. Two ingredients, A and B, are blended to make the fertilizer. Ingredient A is 70% phosphoric acid and 30% potash. Ingredient B is 50% phosphoric acid and 50% potash. If ingredient A costs 30 cents/lb. and ingredient B costs 40 cents/lb., how many pounds of each ingredient should be in each bag of fertilizer in order to achieve the phosphoric acid and potash requirements at minimum cost?*

Person B: List the constraints

Let x = # lbs. of ingredient A (in 1 bag of fertilizer)
Let y = # lbs. of ingredient B (in 1 bag of fertilizer)

Person A check and initial:_____

Person A: Write the objective function.

Person B check and initial:_____

Person B: On a sheet of graph paper, graph TWO of the constraints.

Person A check and initial:_____

Person A: On the same sheet of graph paper, graph the remaining constraints.

Person B check and initial:_____

Person B: List the critical points.

Person A check and initial:_____

Person A: Determine the final solution to the problem.

Person B check and initial:_____

Linear Programming

Names: _____   _____

> *The Wichita Wheelbarrow Company makes two types of wheelbarrows, a utility model and an industrial model. Two machines, A and B, are used in the production of each model. It takes 2 hours on machine A and 3 hours on machine B to produce a dozen of the utility model. It takes 3 hours on machine A and 1 hour on machine B to make a dozen industrial models. Each day there are 9 hours available on machine A and 10 hours available on machine B. If the company makes a $660 per dozen profit on the utility model and $855 per dozen profit on the industrial model, how many dozen of each model should the company produce to maximize profit?*

Person A: List the constraints

Let x = # of utility model (dozens)
Let y = # of industrial model (dozens)

Person B check and initial:_____

Person B: Write the objective function.

Person A check and initial:_____

Person A: On a sheet of graph paper, graph TWO of the constraints.

Person B check and initial:_____

Person B: On the same sheet of graph paper, graph the remaining constraints.

Person A check and initial:_____

Person A: List the critical points.

Person B check and initial:_____

Person B: Determine the final solution to the problem.

Person A check and initial:_____

RoundTable

Steps at a Glance

1. Teacher poses a project, a question with multiple possible answers, or a topic to write about, or a task to which there are many possible solutions, steps, or procedures.

2. In teams, students take turns passing the paper and pencil or team project, each writing one answer or making a contribution.

RoundTable is a lot like RallyCoach (see previous chapter) but it involves four students instead of two. In this structure, students sit in teams of four and number off. There is only one pencil and one piece of paper per group. The teacher poses a problem, either verbally or on paper.

Person 1 begins contributing toward the solution of the problem in writing, and also states aloud what (s)he is doing (i.e. - "I am subtracting 5 from both sides of the equation"). When done, Person 1 passes the paper and pencil to Person 2 who checks the work that has already been done. If it is correct, Person 2 praises Person 1 and writes his/her initials on the paper. If it is incorrect, Person 2 coaches and re-teaches before praising and initialing. Person 2 then picks up where Person 1 left off, continuing toward a solution to the problem in writing and aloud.

ROUNDTABLE

The paper continues around the group in like fashion until a solution is finally reached.

Once teams agree on the final solution to the given problem, they can hand their paper in to the teacher. Another way for students to check their work is to do a "One Stray" activity. The teacher calls a number and that student stands up while the other teammates remain seated and raise their hands. The teacher calls "Stray" and the standing student goes with his/her team's paper to a new team that has their hands up. The teams lower their hands when a new member joins them. The new student on the team presents the work done on the original team and the new teammates give feedback. The students then return to their original teams to share what they learned when they strayed.

RoundTable is useful for...

• Multi-Step problems (as explained above, each person does one step and then passes the paper)

• Proofs (each team member writes a statement and reason)

• Generating Lists (for example, "List all the types of quadrilaterals that have at least one pair of parallel sides.")

Forming Teams: There are many ways to form teams. Teams can be formed randomly by counting off or passing out cards. They can be formed by students themselves or by the teacher. Several problems occur when students form their own teams. First, they tend to join with the same group of friends over and over again. In addition,

RoundTable Contents

PRE-ALGEBRA

- Activities 271
- Blackline Masters 275

ALGEBRA 1

- Activities 281
- Blackline Masters 287

GEOMETRY

- Activities 299
- Blackline Masters 303

ALGEBRA 2

- Activities 309
- Blackline Masters 313

TRIGONOMETRY

- Activities 309
- Blackline Masters 319

PRE-CALCULUS

- Activities 325
- Blackline Masters 331

the special needs students may experience rejection because no one wants them on their team. Finally, you may end up with teams made up entirely of low-ability students or high-ability students.

It is recommended that you use teacher-made heterogeneous groups. A team of four should consist of one student of high ability, one of low ability, and two of average ability (one high-medium, one low-medium). This way, the strongest and weakest students are spread throughout the class and no one is left out. Teams should remain intact for more than one class period so that teambuilding can take place and a mutual support system can develop. The optimal amount of time for teams to stay together is 6 weeks. If the number of students in a class is not divisible by four, make some adjustments…

If one student is left over, create one team of five.

If two students are left over, create two groups of three.

If three students are left over, create one group of three.

On the next several pages you will find many ideas for using RoundTable in your classroom. Blackline masters for some of the suggested activities are also provided. If a team is doing more than one problem on a given topic, have a different person begin the problem each time. This way, the same person isn't doing the same step over and over again. Students will experience more of the various steps necessary to reach a solution.

For more RoundTable activities, refer back to the preceding chapter entitled RallyCoach. Many RallyCoach activities can be modified and used as RoundTable activities, and vice versa.

Cooperative Learning Activities for High School Mathematics
Dina Kushnir

Kagan Publishing • 1 (800) 933-2667
www.KaganOnline.com

Management Tips

1 Only one paper and one pencil per team.

2 You may want to create a record sheet with clearly defined responsibilities for Person 1 and Person 2 etc.. See the blackline masters in this chapter for some examples.

3 Model the gambits for coaching and constructive criticism. For example, "I think you made a calculation error here" or "You left out a vital step here." Students may generate a list of gambits before beginning the activity.

4 Explain and model the difference between coaching and giving the answer.

5 Use teacher-made, heterogeneous groups.

Social Skills

1 Coaching others

2 Patience (giving others time to work)

3 Asking for help

4 Appropriate noise level

5 Offering help

6 Giving and accepting praise

7 Giving and accepting constructive criticism

RoundTable
Pre-Algebra

1. OPERATIONS ON FRACTIONS

Given two fractions, X and Y...

Person 1 - Evaluates X + Y

Person 2 - Evaluates X - Y

Person 3 - Evaluates XY

Person 4 - Evaluates X/Y

$$x = \frac{2}{3}$$

$$y = 1\frac{1}{5}$$

2. OPERATIONS ON DECIMALS

Same as "Operations on Fractions" (above), but students are given two decimals, X and Y, instead of two fractions.

$$x = 7.3$$

$$y = .2$$

3. OPERATIONS ON INTEGERS

Same as "Operations on Fractions" (see activity #1), but students are given two integers, X and Y, instead of two fractions.

x = + 64

y = -4

4. STATISTICS

Given a list of numerical data...

Person 1 - finds the mean

Person 2 - finds the median

Person 3 - finds the mode

Person 4 - Solves a given problem, such as "What score would Joe have to earn on the next test in order to have a mean (average) of 87?"

Below are Joe's test scores in math class.

| 78 | 100 | 86 | 90 | 86 |

5. PROBABILITY

Given the description of an experiment (such as rolling a die)...

Person 1 - finds the number of outcomes in the sample space

Person 2 - Computes the probability of some given event, event A

Person 3 - Computes the probability of some given event, event B

Person 4 - Computes the probability of some given event, event C

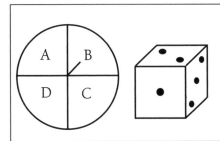

A spinner (shown left) is spun and a six-sided die is tossed simultaneously.

pgs. 277-279

6. ROUNDING

Given a rational number in decimal form...

Person 1 - rounds to the nearest hundredth

Person 2 - rounds to the nearest tenth

Person 3 - rounds to the nearest integer

Person 4 - rounds to the nearest hundred

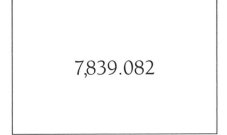

7,839.082

7. INTERPRETING GRAPHS AND OTHER DATA DISPLAYS

Given a graph, table, or other data display, students take turns answering various questions about the information presented in the graph.

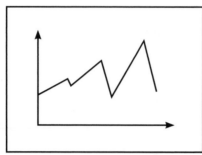

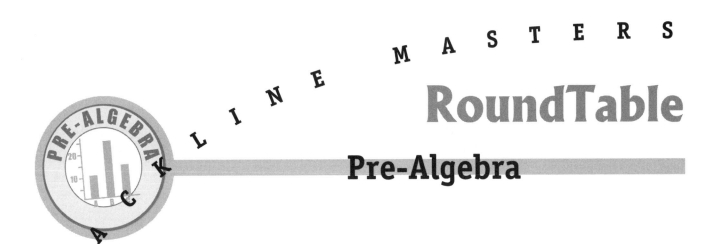

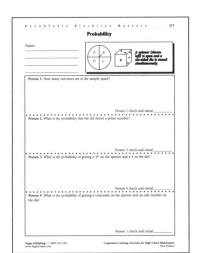

Probability

OBJECTIVES

Given an experiment, and events A and B, students will determine the probability of A, the probability of B, the probability of A or B, and the probability of A and B.

MATERIALS

Pencils and RoundTable worksheets (see following pages)

PREREQUISITE LEARNING

Students should be able to determine the number of outcomes in the sample space, compute the probability of an event A, the probability of event A or event B, and the probability of A and B (both with and without replacement).

FOLLOW-UP ACTIVITY

Once students have determined the theoretical probabilities on their worksheets, they may then conduct the experiments described to see how the theoretical probabilities compare to the actual outcomes after several trials.

Probability

Names:

_____

_____

_____

_____

A spinner (shown left) is spun and a six-sided die is tossed simultaneously.

Person 1: How many outcomes are in the sample space?

Person 2 check and initial:_____

Person 2: What is the probability that the die shows a prime number?

Person 3 check and initial:_____

Person 3: What is the probability of getting a "B" on the spinner and a 4 on the die?

Person 4 check and initial:_____

Person 4: What is the probability of getting a consonant on the spinner and an odd number on the die?

Person 1 check and initial:_____

Kagan Publishing • 1 (800) 933-2667
www.KaganOnline.com

Cooperative Learning Activities for High School Mathematics
Dina Kushnir

Probability

Names:

_____

_____

_____

> *A card is drawn from a standard deck of 52 cards. There are no jokers in the deck.*

Person 1: What is the probability of drawing a red jack?

Person 2 check and initial:_____

Person 2: What is the probability of drawing a black face card or a 9?

Person 3 check and initial:_____

Person 3: What is the probability of drawing a 10 or a king?

Person 4 check and initial:_____

Person 4: What is the probability of drawing a 5 or a diamond?

Person 1 check and initial:_____

Probability

Names:

_____

_____

_____

_____

> *A card is drawn from a standard deck of 52 cards. Without replacing the first card, a second card is drawn. There are no jokers in the deck.*

Person 1: What is the probability of drawing a red jack followed by a 2?

Person 2 check and initial:_____

Person 2: What is the probability of drawing a two kings?

Person 3 check and initial:_____

Person 3: What is the probability of drawing two hearts?

Person 4 check and initial:_____

Person 4: What is the probability of drawing any pair?

Person 1 check and initial:_____

RoundTable

Algebra 1

1. ALGEBRA WORD PROBLEMS IN ONE VARIABLE

Given an algebra word problem...

Person 1 - Establishes the variable (commonly referred to as writing the "let" statements)

Person 2 - Writes an equation based on the information given

Person 3 - Solves the equation

Person 4 - Checks the solution, substitutes the solution back into the "let" statements, and presents a final solution

The word problems chosen by the teacher may be consecutive integer problems, percent problems, age problems, perimeter problems, money problems, or other number problems.

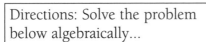

pgs. 288-291

Directions: Solve the problem below algebraically...

Amy is 8 years older than John. In six years, Amy will be twice as old as John will be then. how old are John and Amy now?

Directions: Solve the problem below algebraically...

Find three consecutive integers such that the sum of the first and three times the second is equal to one less than three times the third.

Cooperative Learning Activities for High School Mathematics
Dina Kushnir

2. ALGEBRA WORD PROBLEMS IN TWO VARIABLES (ALGEBRAIC SOLUTION)

Given an algebra word problem...

Person 1 - Writes the "let" statements using two variables

Person 2 - Writes the system of equations needed to solve the problem

Person 3 - Solves for ONE of the variables (using either the "addition method" or the "substitution method")

Person 4 - Solves for the remaining variable

pgs. 295-298

The sum of two numbers is 10. If twice the first number decreased by the second number is 8, find the two numbers.

3. ALGEBRA WORD PROBLEMS IN TWO VARIABLES (GRAPHIC SOLUTION)

Given an algebra word problem...

Person 1 - Writes the "let" statements and the system of equations needed to solve the problem

Person 2 - Graphs one of the equations

Person 3 - Graphs the other equations

Person 4 - States the solution, (x, y), and checks it into the original equations

If you buy 5 sodas and 1 sandwich at the subshop, it will cost $14. It's the same price if you buy 2 sandwiches and 3 sodas. How much is 1 sandwich? How much is 1 soda?

4. Operations on Monomials

Given two monomials, C and D,...

Person 1 - Expresses C+D in simplest form

Person 2 - Expresses C - D in simplest form

Person 3 - Expresses CD in simplest form

Person 4 - Expresses C/D in simplest form

$$C = 7m^2n$$
$$D = -2mn^3$$

5. Operations on Polynomials

Same as "Operations on Monomials," except the teams are given two polynomials, C and D, instead of monomials.

$$C = x^2 - 4x - 32$$
$$D = x - 8$$

6. Operations on Rational Expressions (also known as "Algebraic Fractions")

Students express in lowest terms...

Person 1 - the product of two given rational expressions

Person 2 - the sum of two given rational expressions

Person 3 - the quotient of two given rational expressions

Person 4 - the difference of two given rational expressions

The rational expressions used in these problems may have monomial or polynomial denomenators, depending on what point students have reached in their coursework.

$$\frac{5}{x-4} \ , \ \frac{7}{x}$$

7. Writing the Equation of a Line

Given three points, $A(x_1, y_1)$, $B(x_2, y_2)$, and $C(x_3, y_3)$...

Person 1 - Finds the slope of the line passing through A and B

Person 2 - Writes the equation of line $\overleftrightarrow{AB}$

Person 3 - Writes the equation of the line parallel to $\overleftrightarrow{AB}$ and passing through C

Person 4 - Writes the equation of the line perpendicular to $\overleftrightarrow{AB}$ and passing through C

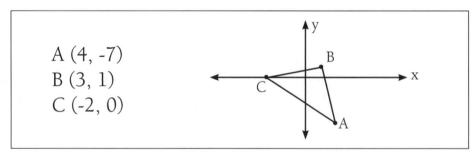

A (4, -7)
B (3, 1)
C (-2, 0)

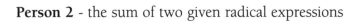

8. Operations on Radicals

Express in simplest radical form...

Person 1 - the product of two given radical expressions in the form $a\sqrt{b}$

Person 2 - the sum of two given radical expressions

Person 3 - the quotient of two given radical expressions

Person 4 - the square of a given radical expression

Note: This activity can be modified to include expressions in the form $a + b\sqrt{c}$

$$7\sqrt{2} \ , 2\sqrt{8}$$

9. Solving Quadratic Equations

Given a quadratic equation...

Person 1 - Rewrites the equation in standard form ($ax^2 + bx + c = 0$)

Person 2 - Factors completely

Person 3 - Solves for x and checks the solutions

$$x^2 + 5x = 2(x - 1)$$

MASTERS

RoundTable

Algebra 1

Solving Algebra Word Problems with One Variable

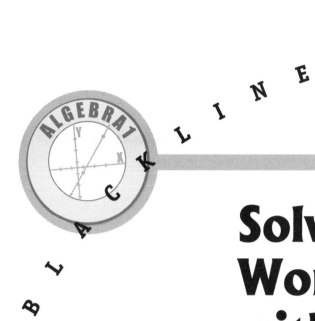

OBJECTIVES

Given a word problem, students will establish variables, write an equation, solve the equation, and use their result to answer the question posed.

MATERIALS

Pencils and RoundTable worksheets (see following pages)

PREREQUISITE LEARNING

Students should be able to solve linear equations in one variable and write algebraic expressions based on verbally presented problems.

POSSIBLE EXTENSION

Once students have mastered solving word problems which require the solution of linear equations, they may then be presented with problems which require solving a quadratic equation.

Solving Algebra Word Problems with One Variable

Names:

_____

_____

_____

_____

> **Directions: Solve the problem below algebraically...**
>
> *Amy is 8 years older than John. In six years, Amy will be twice as old as John will be then. How old are John and Amy now?*

Person 1: Establish the variables ("let" statements)

Person 2 check and initial:_____

Person 2: Write the equation needed to solve he problem. (Do not solve it)

Person 3 check and initial:_____

Person 3: Solve the equation

Person 4 check and initial:_____

Person 4: Substitute back into the "let" statements to answer the original question

Person 1 check and initial:_____

Solving Algebra Word Problems with One Variable

Names:

_____

_____

_____

_____

Directions: Solve the problem below algebraically...
Find three consecutive integers such that the sum of
the first and three times the second is equal to one less
than three times the third.

Person 1: Establish the variables ("let" statements)

Person 2 check and initial:_____

Person 2: Write the equation needed to solve the problem. (Do not solve it)

Person 3 check and initial:_____

Person 3: Solve the equation

Person 4 check and initial:_____

Person 4: Substitute back into the "let" statements to answer the original question

Person 1 check and initial:_____

Kagan Publishing • 1 (800) 933-2667
www.KaganOnline.com

Cooperative Learning Activities for High School Mathematics
Dina Kushnir

Solving Algebra Word Problems with One Variable

Names:

_____

_____

_____

_____

> *Directions: Solve the problem below algebraically...*
>
> *△ABC is isosceles, with base $\overline{AC}$. If m∠B is 20 degrees more than twice m ∠A find the measures of all three angles in the triangle.*

Person 1: Establish the variables ("let" statements or a labeled diagram)

Person 2 check and initial:_____

Person 2: Write the equation needed to solve the problem. (Do not solve it)

Person 3 check and initial:_____

Person 3: Solve the equation

Person 4 check and initial:_____

Person 4: Substitute back into the "let" statements to answer the original question

Person 1 check and initial:_____

Solving Algebra Word Problems with One Variable

Names:

_____

_____

_____

_____

> **Directions: Solve the problem below algebraically...**

Person 1: Establish the variables ("let" statements or a labeled diagram)

Person 2 check and initial:_____

· ·

Person 2: Write the equation needed to solve the problem. (Do not solve it)

Person 3 check and initial:_____

· ·

Person 3: Solve the equation

Person 4 check and initial:_____

· ·

Person 4: Substitute back into the "let" statements to answer the original question

Person 1 check and initial:_____

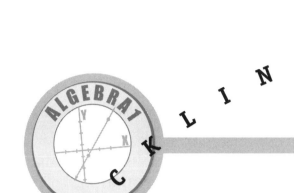

ALGEBRA 1

B L A C K L I N E M A S T E R S

RoundTable
Algebra 1

Solving Algebra Word Problems with a System of Equations

OBJECTIVES

Given a word problem, students will establish two variables, write a system of two linear equations, solve the system, and use their result to answer the question posed.

MATERIALS

Pencils and RoundTable Worksheets (see following pages)

PREREQUISITE LEARNING

Students should be able to write algebraic equations based on verbally presented problems. They should also be able to solve a system of two linear equations using the addition method and/or the substitution method.

Kagan Publishing • 1 (800) 933-2667
www.KaganOnline.com

Cooperative Learning Activities for High School Mathematics
Dina Kushnir

POSSIBLE EXTENSION

Once students have mastered solving a system of equations algebraically, they can then solve a system of equations graphically. New RoundTable worksheets can be created for graphic solutions (Person 1 establishes the variables, Person 2 writes the equations, Person 3 graphs one equation, Person 4 graphs the second equation, Person 1 determines the solution and checks it). For problems whose solutions involve decimals, problems can be solved using a graphing calculator.

Solving Algebra Word Problems with a System of Equations

Names:

_____

_____

_____

_____

> **Directions: Solve the problem below algebraically using TWO variables...**
>
> *One day Phil purchased 5 loaves of bread and 3 muffins for a total of $8.00. A few days later, at the same store, he purchased 2 loaves of bread and 6 muffins for a total of $5.60. What is the price of a single loaf of bread and a single muffin?*

Person 1: Establish the variables ("let" statements)

Person 2 check and initial:_____

Person 2: Write the system of equations needed to solve the problem. (Do not solve it)

Person 3 check and initial:_____

Person 3: Solve the system of equations for <u>one variable only!</u>

Person 4 check and initial:_____

Person 4: Solve for the remaining variable

Person 1 check and initial:_____

Solving Algebra Word Problems with a System of Equations

Names:

_____

_____

_____

_____

> **Directions: Solve the problem below algebraically using TWO variables...**
>
> *Freeport High sold tickets for a school musical. Orchestra seats cost $6 each and balcony seats cost $4 each. A total of 200 tickets was sold and $960 was collected. How many of each type of ticket was sold?*

Person 1: Establish the variables ("let" statements)

Person 2 check and initial:_____

Person 2: Write the system of equations needed to solve the problem. (Do not solve it)

Person 3 check and initial:_____

Person 3: Solve the system of equations for <u>one variable only!</u>

Person 4 check and initial:_____

Person 4: Solve for the remaining variable

Person 1 check and initial:_____

Solving Algebra Word Problems with a System of Equations

Names:

_____

_____

_____

_____

> *Directions: Solve the problem below algebraically using TWO variables...*
>
> *Renee collects baseball cards and football cards. The number of baseball cards is 10 more than twice the number of football cards. All together, Renee has 70 cards. How many of each type of card does Renee have?*

Person 1: Establish the variables ("let" statements)

Person 2 check and initial:_____

Person 2: Write the system of equations needed to solve the problem. (Do not solve it)

Person 3 check and initial:_____

Person 3: Solve the system of equations for <u>one variable only!</u>

Person 4 check and initial:_____

Person 4: Use substitution to solve for the remaining variable.

Person 1 check and initial:_____

Cooperative Learning Activities for High School Mathematics
Dina Kushnir

Solving Algebra Word Problems with a System of Equations

Names:

_____

_____

_____

_____

> **Directions: Solve the problem below algebraically using TWO variables...**

Person 1: Establish the variables ("let" statements)

Person 2 check and initial:_____

Person 2: Write the equation needed to solve the problem. (Do not solve it)

Person 3 check and initial:_____

Person 3: Solve the system of equations for <u>one variable only!</u>

Person 4 check and initial:_____

Person 4: Use substitution to solve for the remaining variable.

Person 1 check and initial:_____

RoundTable

Geometry

1. CONSTRUCTIONS

Each team gets a compass and straight edge. At the top of a piece of paper, a triangle labeled ABC is drawn. Point D lies on $\overline{AB}$.

Person 1 - Constructs a triangle congruent to the given △ABC

Person 2 - Constructs the bisector of ∠ B

Person 3 - Constructs a line perpendicular to $\overline{AB}$ and passing through point D

Person 4 - Constructs a line parallel to $\overline{AB}$ and passing through C

Many variations of this activity are possible, depending on how many constructions the students have been taught.

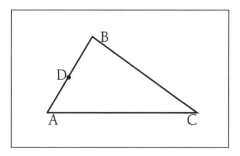

Cooperative Learning Activities for High School Mathematics
Dina Kushnir

2. GEOMETRY PROOFS

Each team is given a geometry proof with some given information. Person 1 draws a diagram based on the given information. The paper is then passed to person 2, who writes two steps (statement and reason) of the proof. The paper is then passed to person 3, who writes two more steps. The paper continues to go around the table until the proof is complete.

This activity can be done for all kinds of proofs: Congruent triangle proofs, Inequality proofs, Quadrilateral proofs, Similar triangle proofs, Addition and Subtraction Postulates, Overlapping triangle proofs, Parallel line proofs, Circle proofs, etc.

Prove that the altitude to the base of an isosceles triangle bisects the base of the triangle.

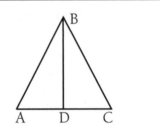

3. CIRCLE PROBLEMS

Each team is given a diagram of a circle with some given information regarding arc lengths, angle measures, relationships between chords, lengths of chords, etc. Using the circle theorems, students take turns finding new measurements in the diagram based on the given information.

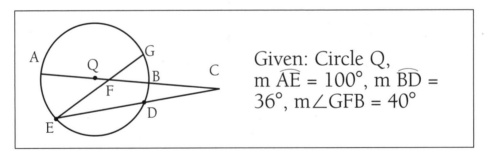

Given: Circle Q, m $\widehat{AE}$ = 100°, m $\widehat{BD}$ = 36°, m∠GFB = 40°

4. GEOMETRY DEFINITIONS

Students are given a list of 8 poorly written or incomplete geometry definitions. (For example: "A parallelogram is a four sided figure" or "M is the midpoint of $\overline{AB}$ if M lies on $\overline{AB}$.") Students take turns improving or re-writing these definitions so that they are complete and accurate.

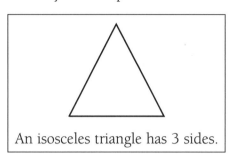

An isosceles triangle has 3 sides.

5. GEOMETRY DEFINITIONS (WITH DIAGRAM)

Each team is given a geometry diagram such as the one below...

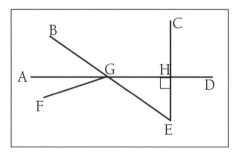

Students are then asked to answer various questions about the diagram which test their mastery of some basic geometry definitions. For example...

Person 1 - Name 4 acute angles in this diagram

Person 2 - Name 3 obtuse angles in this diagram

Person 3 - Which angles are supplementary?

Person 4 - Name 3 pairs of adjacent angles

Person 1 - Name two pairs of vertical angles

Person 2 - Which angles form a "linear pair"

Person 3 - Is there an angle bisector in this diagram? If so, indicate the bisector and the angle it bisects

Person 4 - Which lines in this diagram are perpendicular

6. QUADRILATERALS

Students are given a list of 8 statements regarding the properties quadrilaterals. For example: "A rhombus has congruent diagonals" or "A square is a rectangle." Students must decide whether each statement is "always true," "sometimes true," or "never true." They must also justify their answer with a short written explanation or diagram. Students pass the paper around as each problem is completed.

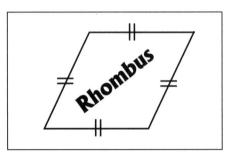

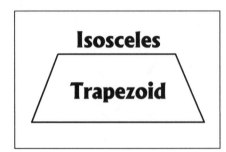

7. SIMILAR RIGHT TRIANGLES

Each team is given a diagram which includes at least one of the following: an altitude drawn to the hypotenuse of a right triangle, a 30 - 60 - 90 triangle, or a 45 - 45 - 90 triangle. Some examples are shown below...

pgs. 305-307

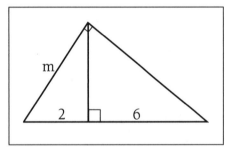

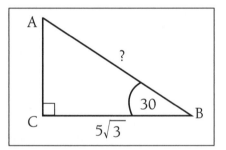

Students use "geometric means" or "special right triangle ratios" to find various measurements in the diagram. (For example: "Find m" or "Find the length of $\overline{AB}$ in simplest radical form.")

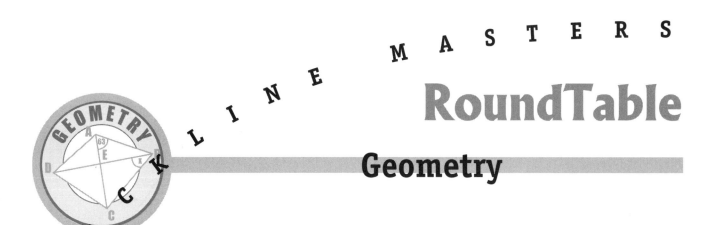

M A S T E R S

RoundTable

Geometry

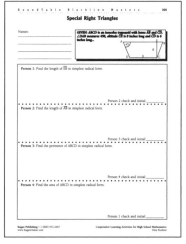

Special Right Triangles

OBJECTIVES

Given a geometric diagram involving right triangles (including 30-60-90 and 45-45-90 triangles), students will find the lengths of various line segments in the diagram. Methods for finding these lengths will include use of special right triangle ratios, geometric means, Pythagorean theorem, and proportions.

MATERIALS

Pencils and RoundTable Worksheets (see next pages)

PREREQUISITE LEARNING

Students need to know the relationships between the sides of 30-60-90 triangles and 45-45-90 triangles, as shown below...

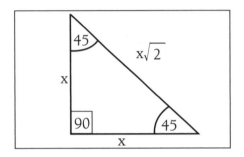

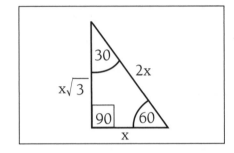

Second, they should be familiar with the proportions which exist when an altitude is drawn to the hypotenuse of a right triangle...

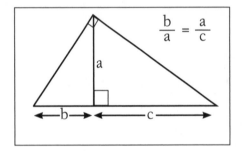

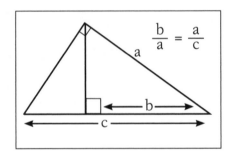

Finally, students should be aware of other geometric problem solving strategies, including use of the Pythagorean theorem and setting up proportions between the corresponding sides of similar triangles.

POSSIBLE EXTENSIONS

The diagrams in these RoundTable activities can be as simple or complex as the teacher sees fit. Other concepts which can be integrated into these activities include right triangle trigonometry, parallel line theorems, circle theorems, and properties of various quadrilaterals.

Special Right Triangles

Names:

_____

_____

_____

_____

> **GIVEN: ABCD is an isosceles trapezoid with bases $\overline{AB}$ and $\overline{CD}$.**
> $\angle DAB$ measures 45°, altitude $\overline{CE}$ is 8 inches long and $\overline{CD}$ is 6 inches long...

Person 1: Find the length of $\overline{EB}$ in simplest radical form.

Person 2 check and initial:_____

Person 2: Find the length of $\overline{AB}$ in simplest radical form.

Person 3 check and initial:_____

Person 3: Find the perimeter of ABCD in simplest radical form.

Person 4 check and initial:_____

Person 4: Find the area of ABCD in simplest radical form.

Person 1 check and initial:_____

Kagan Publishing • 1 (800) 933-2667
www.KaganOnline.com

Cooperative Learning Activities for High School Mathematics
Dina Kushnir

Special Right Triangles

Names:

_____

_____

_____

_____

> **GIVEN: ABC is a right triangle with a right angle at C. $\overline{CD}$ is the altitude drawn to the hypotenuse. ∠CAD measures 30°. AC = 12.**
>

Person 1: Find the length of $\overline{AD}$ in simplest radical form.

Person 2 check and initial:_____

• •

Person 2: Find the length of $\overline{DC}$ in simplest radical form.

Person 3 check and initial:_____

• •

Person 3: Find the length of $\overline{DB}$ in simplest radical form.

Person 4 check and initial:_____

• •

Person 4: Find the length of $\overline{BC}$ in simplest radical form.

Person 1 check and initial:_____

Special Right Triangles

Names:

_____

_____

_____

_____

> *GIVEN: ABC is a right triangle with hypotenuse $\overline{AB}$. $\overline{DE}$ is parallel to $\overline{CB}$. $\angle B$ measures 60°, DE = 2, and AC = 3 $\sqrt{3}$*

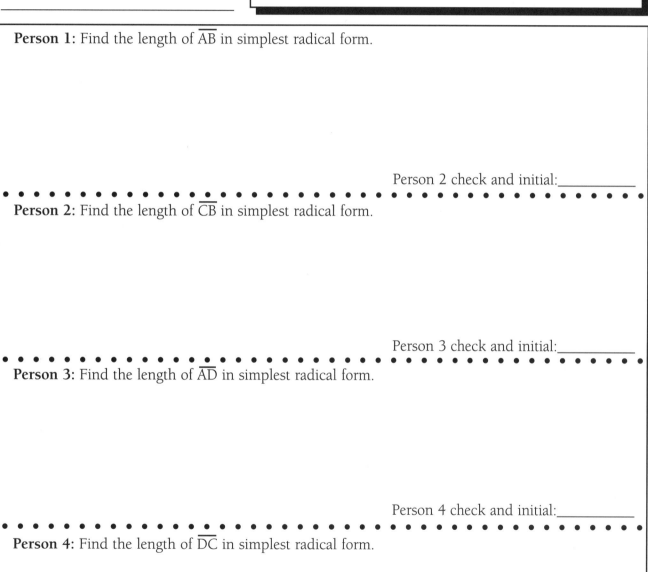

Person 1: Find the length of $\overline{AB}$ in simplest radical form.

Person 2 check and initial:_____

• •

Person 2: Find the length of $\overline{CB}$ in simplest radical form.

Person 3 check and initial:_____

• •

Person 3: Find the length of $\overline{AD}$ in simplest radical form.

Person 4 check and initial:_____

• •

Person 4: Find the length of $\overline{DC}$ in simplest radical form.

Person 1 check and initial:_____

Cooperative Learning Activities for High School Mathematics
Dina Kushnir

RoundTable

Algebra 2 and Trigonometry

1. COORDINATE GEOMETRY

Given 2 points, A(x1, y1) and B(x2, y2) ...

Person 1 - Finds the slope of the line passing through A and B

Person 2 - Finds the length of $\overline{AB}$ in simplest radical form

Person 3 - Finds the midpoint of $\overline{AB}$

Person 4 - Writes the equation of the perpendicular bisector of $\overline{AB}$

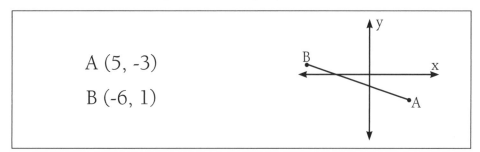

A (5, -3)

B (-6, 1)

2. COMPOSITIONS AND INVERSES OF FUNCTIONS

Given two functions, f(x) and g(x)...

Person 1 - Writes a rule for f(g(x))

Person 2 - Writes a rule for g(f(x))

Person 3 - Writes a rule for $f^{-1}(x)$

Person 4 - Writes a rule for $g^{-1}(x)$

pgs. 315-318

$$f(x) = x^2$$
$$g(x) = 3x - 1$$

$$f(x) = \sqrt{x + 5}$$
$$g(x) = 2x^2 - 3$$

3. TRIGONOMETRIC FUNCTIONS ON THE NON-UNIT CIRCLE

Students are given one trigonometric value of a given angle, ∡A, and a clue regarding which quadrant contains ∡A. Using this information, students must take turns finding other trig function values.

pgs. 321-323

$$\sin A = \frac{7}{11}$$
$$\angle A \in QII$$

4. TRANSFORMATIONS ON THE COORDINATE PLANE

Students are given a piece of graph paper and the coordinates of the vertices of △ABC

Person 1 - Plot and label △ABC Reflect this triangle over the x-axis and label it △A'B'C'

Person 2 - Reflect △A'B'C' over the line y = x. Label this new triangle △A"B"C"

Person 3 - Reflect △A"B"C" through the point (- 4, 3). Label this new triangle △A'''B'''C'''

Person 4 - Find the image of △A'''B'''C''' under the translation T$_{3,7}$. Label the new triangle △A''''B''''C''''

Note: This activity can be modified to include dilations, rotations about the origin, rotations not centered about the origin, reflections over lines in the form y = k or x = k, reflections over the line y = - x, point reflections through the origin, etc.

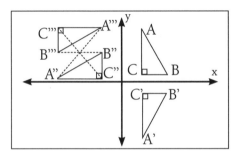

5. COMPLEX NUMBERS

Given two complex numbers in a + bi form...

Person 1 - finds the sum of the two complex numbers

Person 2 - finds the product of the two complex numbers

Person 3 - finds the quotient of the two complex numbers

Person 4 - finds the square of the first complex number

$$-7 + 2i$$
$$3 - i$$

6. TRIGONOMETRIC GRAPHS

Given an equation in the form y = asinbx or y = acosbx...

Person 1 - determines the amplitude of the graph

Person 2 - determines the frequency of the graph

Person 3 - determines the period of the graph

Person 4 - sketches the graph from $0 \leq x \leq 2\pi$

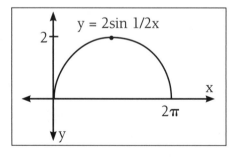

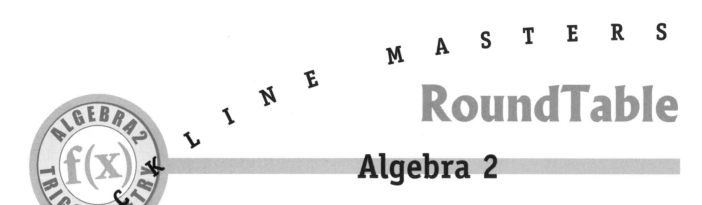

RoundTable
Algebra 2

Compositions of Functions and Inverses of Functions

OBJECTIVES

Given an equation for f(x) and g(x), students will write an equation for f(g(x)), g(f(x)), f $^{-1}$ (x), and g $^{-1}$ (x).

MATERIALS

Pencils and RoundTable worksheets (see following pages)

PREREQUISITE LEARNING

Students should be familiar with function notation, evaluating functions, and writing equations for function compositions and inverses.

Kagan Publishing • 1 (800) 933-2667
www.KaganOnline.com

Cooperative Learning Activities for High School Mathematics
Dina Kushnir

FOLLOW-UP ACTIVITY

In their groups of four, students can work together to make up their own f(x) and g(x) on a blank RoundTable worksheet. They can then trade sheets with a nearby group to write all the indicated compositions and inverses. Students can then trade back papers to check each others work. Checking can also be done as a RoundTable (Person 1 checks problem 1, Person 2 checks problem 2, etc).

Compositions of Functions and Inverses of Functions

Names:

_____

_____

_____

_____

GIVEN:

$f(x) = 2x - 5$

$g(x) = -3x + 4$

Person 1: Write a rule for f(g(x)) in simplest algebraic form.

Person 2 check and initial:_____

Person 2: Write a rule for g(f(x)) in simplest algebraic form.

Person 3 check and initial:_____

Person 3: Write a rule for $f^{-1}(x)$ in simplest algebraic form.

Person 4 check and initial:_____

Person 4: Write a rule for $g^{-1}(x)$ in simplest algebraic form.

Person 1 check and initial:_____

Compositions of Functions and Inverses of Functions

Names:

_____

_____

_____

_____

GIVEN:

$$f(x) = x + 3$$

$$g(x) = 2x^2 - 7$$

Person 1: Write a rule for f(g(x)) in simplest algebraic form.

Person 2 check and initial:_____

Person 2: Write a rule for g(f(x)) in simplest algebraic form.

Person 3 check and initial:_____

Person 3: Write a rule for $f^{-1}(x)$ in simplest algebraic form.

Person 4 check and initial:_____

Person 4: Write a rule for $g^{-1}(x)$ in simplest algebraic form.

Person 1 check and initial:_____

Compositions of Functions and Inverses of Functions

Names:

_____

_____

_____

_____

GIVEN:

$$f(x) = x^2 + 4$$

$$g(x) = \sqrt{x - 8}$$

Person 1: Write a rule for f(g(x)) in simplest algebraic form.

Person 2 check and initial:_____

Person 2: Write a rule for g(f(x)) in simplest algebraic form.

Person 3 check and initial:_____

Person 3: Write a rule for f⁻¹(x) in simplest algebraic form.

Person 4 check and initial:_____

Person 4: Write a rule for g⁻¹(x) in simplest algebraic form.

Person 1 check and initial:_____

Compositions of Functions and Inverses of Functions

Names:

_____

_____

_____

_____

> **GIVEN:**
>
> $f(x) =$
>
> $g(x) =$

Person 1: Write a rule for f(g(x)) in simplest algebraic form.

Person 2 check and initial:_____

Person 2: Write a rule for g(f(x)) in simplest algebraic form.

Person 3 check and initial:_____

Person 3: Write a rule for $f^{-1}(x)$ in simplest algebraic form.

Person 4 check and initial:_____

Person 4: Write a rule for $g^{-1}(x)$ in simplest algebraic form.

Person 1 check and initial:_____

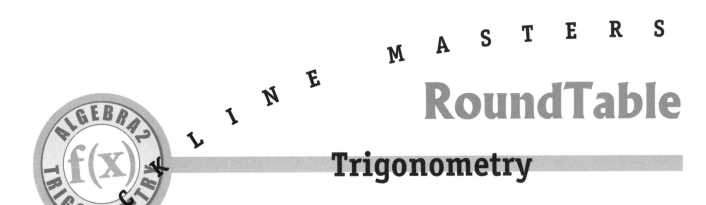

M A S T E R S

RoundTable
Trigonometry

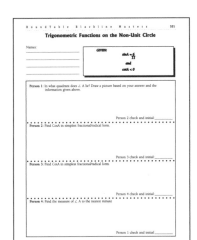

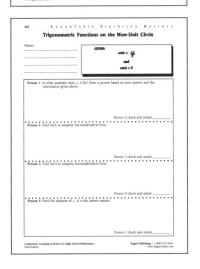

Trigonometric Functions on the Non-Unit Circle

OBJECTIVES

Given one trigonometric value of an angle, students will determine other trigonometric values of the angle and the measure of the angle.

MATERIALS

Pencils, scientific calculators, and RoundTable worksheets (see following pages)

PREREQUISITE LEARNING

Students should be familiar with the unit circle and the non-unit circle, the six trig functions, and the signs of various trig functions in all four quadrants. Students should also be able to apply the Pythagorean Theorem to find the missing side of a right triangle and express answers in simplest radical form. Finally, students should be able to use the inverse trig functions on their scientific calculators and convert decimal degrees to degrees, minutes, and seconds.

Trigonometric Functions on the Non-Unit Circle

Names:

_____

_____

_____

_____

GIVEN:

$$sinA = \frac{6}{11}$$

and

$$cotA < 0$$

Person 1: In what quadrant does $\angle$ A lie? Draw a picture based on your answer and the information given above.

Person 2 check and initial:_____

Person 2: Find CosA in simplest fractional/radical form.

Person 3 check and initial:_____

Person 3: Find CotA in simplest fractional/radical form.

Person 4 check and initial:_____

Person 4: Find the measure of $\angle$ A to the nearest minute

Person 1 check and initial:_____

Trigonometric Functions on the Non-Unit Circle

Names:

_____

_____

_____

_____

> **GIVEN:**
>
> $$cotA = \frac{-12}{5}$$
>
> *and*
>
> $$cosA > 0$$

Person 1: In what quadrant does ∠ A lie? Draw a picture based on your answer and the information given above.

Person 2 check and initial:_____

Person 2: Find SinA in simplest fractional/radical form.

Person 3 check and initial:_____

Person 3: Find SecA in simplest fractional/radical form.

Person 4 check and initial:_____

Person 4: Find the measure of ∠ A to the nearest minute

Person 1 check and initial:_____

Cooperative Learning Activities for High School Mathematics
Dina Kushnir

Kagan Publishing • 1 (800) 933-2667
www.KaganOnline.com

Trigonometric Functions on the Non-Unit Circle

Names:

_____

_____

_____

_____

> **GIVEN:**
>
> $$cscA = \frac{-15}{8}$$
>
> *and*
>
> *cosA < 0*

Person 1: In what quadrant does ∠ A lie? Draw a picture based on your answer and the information given above.

Person 2 check and initial:_____

Person 2: Find TanA in simplest fractional/radical form.

Person 3 check and initial:_____

Person 3: Find SecA in simplest fractional/radical form.

Person 4 check and initial:_____

Person 4: Find the measure of ∠ A to the nearest minute

Person 1 check and initial:_____

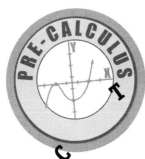

RoundTable

Pre-Calculus

1. SOLVING SYSTEMS OF EQUATIONS USING DETERMINANTS

Given a system of equations with variables, x and y...

Person 1 - finds the value of the determinant D

Person 2 - finds the value of the determinant D_x

Person 3 - finds the value of the determinant D_y

Person 4 - uses the above answers to find the values of x and y

$$4x + 7y = 15$$
$$-3x + 5y = 12$$

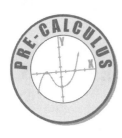

2. Domain and Range of a Function

Given an equation for f(x)...

Person 1 - graphs y = f(x) on a graphing calculator

Person 2 - determines the domain of f(x), either algebraically or using the graph

Person 3 - determines the range of f(x), either algebraically or using the graph

$$y = \frac{5}{3 + x}$$

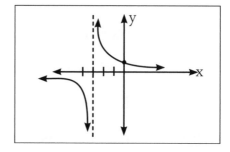

3. Coordinate Geometry

Given a circle whose diameter has endpoints $P(x_1, y_1)$ and $Q(x_2, y_2)$...

Person 1 - determines the coordinates of the center of the circle

Person 2 - determines the radius of the circle in simplest radical form

Person 3 - writes the equation of the circle

Person 4 - determines whether or not the given circle passes through a third given

point, $R(x_3, y_3)$

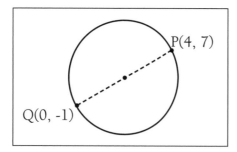

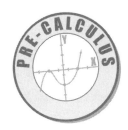

4. INTERVAL FUNCTIONS

Given an equation in the form $y = \begin{cases} f(x)\,;\, x < a \\ g(x)\,;\, a \leq x < b \\ h(x)\,;\, b \leq x < c \\ j(x)\,;\, x \geq c \end{cases}$

Person 1 - graphs f(x) on a piece of graph paper

Person 2 - graphs g(x) on the same coordinate plane

Person 3 - graphs h(x) on the same coordinate plane

Person 4 - graphs j(x) on the same coordinate plane

$$y= \begin{cases} 4,\, x < -2 \\ |x + 1|,\, -2 \leq x \leq 2 \\ x^2 - 6x + 11,\, 2 < x \leq 5 \\ -2x + 16,\, x > 5 \end{cases}$$

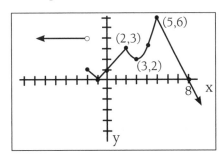

5. GRAPHING RATIONAL FUNCTIONS

Given an equation such as $y = \dfrac{2\,(x\text{-}3)^2\,(x\text{+}2)}{(x\text{-}5)\,(x\text{+}3)^2}$

Person 1 - determines the x-intercepts and y-intercept

Person 2 - determines the equations of vertical asymptotes

Person 3 - determines the equation of the horizontal or diagonal asymptote

Person 4 - sketches a graph of the given rational function

pgs. 333-337

$$y = \frac{3(x + 1)^2\,(x - 2)}{(x + 3)\,(x - 1)^2}$$

6. DISCRIMINANT AND THE ROOTS OF A QUADRATIC EQUATION

Given an equation such as $0 = kx^2 - 6x + 5$ or $x^2 + 2x + k = 0$...

Person 1 - determines a value of k so that the roots are real, rational, and unequal

Person 2 - determines a value of k so that the roots are real, rational, and equal

Person 3 - determines a value of k so that the roots are real, irrational, and unequal

Person 4 - determines a value of k so that the roots are imaginary

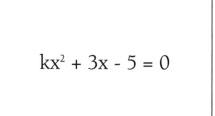

$$kx^2 + 3x - 5 = 0$$

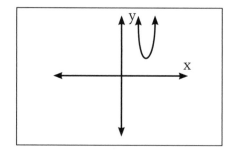

7. INTERPRETING FUNCTION GRAPHS

Given a graph for some function $y = f(x)$, students take turns answering questions such as...

Find $f(2)$.

For which value of x does $f(x) = 3$?

Which is larger, $f(0)$ or $f(-1)$?

Is 5 in the range of $f(x)$?

Does $f(x) = f(-x)$ for all x in the domain?

What is the average rate of change for $f(x)$ on the interval $[-1, 3]$?

The types of questions used can be modified depending on where students are in their study of function graphs.

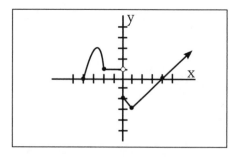

8. TRANSFORMATIONS OF FUNCTIONS

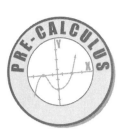

Given a graph of some function $y = f(x)$...

Person 1 - sketches the graph of $y = 2f(x)$

Person 2 - sketches the graph of $y = |f(x)|$

Person 3 - sketches the graph of $y = f(x) + 3$

Person 4 - sketches the graph of $y = f(x - 1)$

It is recommended that a new coordinate plane is drawn for each graph. This activity can be modified to include graphs of $-f(x)$, $f(-x)$, $f(1/2\ x)$, $f^{-1}(x)$, etc.

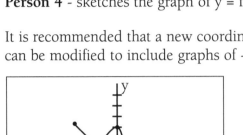

9. COMPOSITIONS OF FUNCTIONS

Given $f(x) = \frac{1}{x}$, $g(x) = \sqrt{x}$, $h(x) = 2x+1$, and $j(x) = x^2$...

Person 1 - expresses $a(x) = 2x^2 + 1$ as the composition of two of the given functions

Person 2 - expresses $b(x) = \frac{2}{x} + 1$ as the composition of two of the given functions

Person 3 - expresses $c(x) = \sqrt{\frac{1}{x}}$ as the composition of two of the given functions

Person 4 - expresses $d(x) = \frac{1}{x^2}$ as the composition of two of the given functions

$$f(x) = \frac{1}{x}$$
$$g(x) = \sqrt{x}$$
$$h(x) = 2x + 1$$
$$j(x) = x^2$$

10. WRITING FUNCTIONS

A rectangle is inscribed in a circle of diameter 12 cm. The width of the rectangle is x.

Person 1 - expresses the length of the rectangle in terms of x

Person 2 - expresses the area of the rectangle in terms of x

Person 3 - expresses the perimeter of the rectangle in terms of x

Person 4 - expresses the area of the shaded space in terms of x

This activity can be modified to included countless different types of word problems.

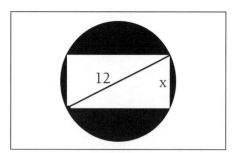

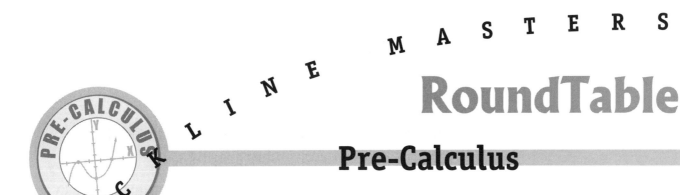

B L A C K L I N E   M A S T E R S

RoundTable
Pre-Calculus

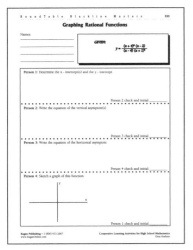

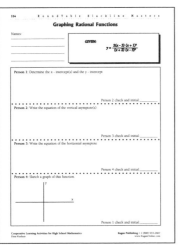

Graphing Rational Functions

OBJECTIVES

Students will graph functions in the form of $y = \dfrac{p(x)}{q(x)}$, where $p(x)$ and $q(x)$ are polynomials in factored form.

MATERIALS

Pencils and RoundTable worksheets (see following pages)

PREREQUISITE LEARNING

Students should be able to determine the x-intercepts, y-intercepts, vertical asymptotes, and horizontal asymptotes of a rational function. They should also be familiar with how the multiplicity of a factor affects the graph of the function.

FOLLOW-UP ACTIVITY

Once students have mastered graphing rational functions, two follow-up activities are possible:

1. Students may attempt to write a rational function based on a given graph.

2. Students can learn to graph a rational function with a diagonal asymptote, and then complete a RoundTable Activity on graphing such a function.

Graphing Rational Functions

Names:

_____

_____

_____

_____

GIVEN:

$$y = \frac{(x + 4)^2 (x - 2)}{(x - 4) (x + 1)^2}$$

Person 1: Determine the x-intercept(s) and the y-intercept

Person 2 check and initial:_____

Person 2: Write the equation of the vertical asymptote(s)

Person 3 check and initial:_____

Person 3: Write the equation of the horizontal asymptote

Person 4 check and initial:_____

Person 4: Sketch a graph of this function.

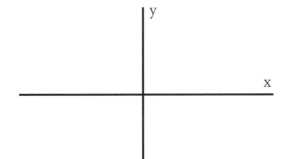

Person 1 check and initial:_____

Graphing Rational Functions

Names:

_____

_____

_____

_____

GIVEN:

$$y = \frac{2(x-3)(x+1)^2}{(x+2)(x-5)^2}$$

Person 1: Determine the x-intercept(s) and the y-intercept

Person 2 check and initial:_____

· ·

Person 2: Write the equation of the vertical asymptote(s)

Person 3 check and initial:_____

· ·

Person 3: Write the equation of the horizontal asymptote

Person 4 check and initial:_____

· ·

Person 4: Sketch a graph of this function.

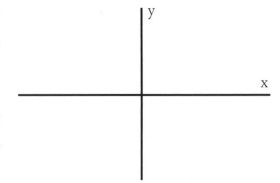

Person 1 check and initial:_____

Graphing Rational Functions

Names:

_____

_____

_____

_____

> **GIVEN:**
>
> $$y = \frac{2(x + 6)\,(x - 2)^2}{(x + 4)^2\,(x - 1)^2\,(x + 1)}$$

Person 1: Determine the x-intercept(s) and the y-intercept

Person 2 check and initial:_____

Person 2: Write the equation of the vertical asymptote(s)

Person 3 check and initial:_____

Person 3: Write the equation of the horizontal asymptote

Person 4 check and initial:_____

Person 4: Sketch a graph of this function.

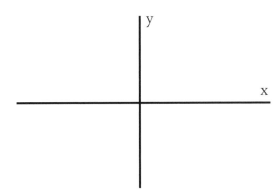

Person 1 check and initial:_____

Cooperative Learning Activities for High School Mathematics
Dina Kushnir

Graphing Rational Functions

Names:

_____

_____

_____

_____

GIVEN:

$y =$

Person 1:   Determine the x-intercept(s) and the y-intercept

Person 2 check and initial:_____

Person 2:   Write the equation of the vertical asymptote(s)

Person 3 check and initial:_____

Person 3:   Write the equation of the horizontal asymptote

Person 4 check and initial:_____

Person 4:   Sketch a graph of this function.

Person 1 check and initial:_____

Graphing Rational Functions

Names:

_____

_____

_____

_____

GIVEN:

$$y = \frac{(x + 3)(x - 1)^*}{x + 1}$$

*This function has a <u>diagonal</u> asymptote

Person 1: Determine the x-intercept(s) and the y-intercept

Person 2 check and initial:_____

Person 2: Determine the equation of the vertical asymptote

Person 3 check and initial:_____

Person 3: Determine the equation of the diagonal asymptote

Person 4 check and initial:_____

Person 4: Sketch a graph of this function.

Person 1 check and initial:_____

Kagan Publishing • 1 (800) 933-2667
www.KaganOnline.com

Cooperative Learning Activities for High School Mathematics
Dina Kushnir

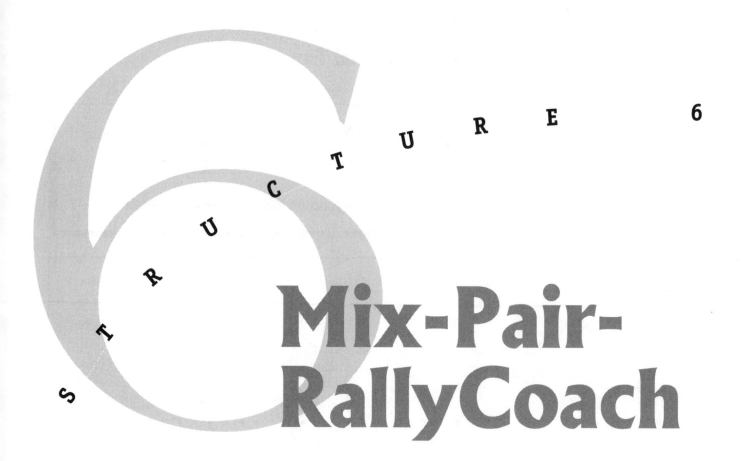

Mix-Pair-RallyCoach

Steps at a Glance

1. Students "Mix" around the room.

2. Teacher calls, "Pair."

3. Student pair up.

4. Partner A solves the problem while Partner B watches, checks, and praises.

5. Partner B solves the problem while Partner A watches, checks, and praises.

6. Pairs check their work by handing paper into the teacher or checking with another pair.

7. Repeat with new problems.

In this structure, each student is given a card containing some information. Students are to "mix" (that is, mingle around the room) and form pairs, Person A and Person B. The two students combine the information on their cards to solve problems posed by the teacher. Person A and person B are each given unique problems to solve, thus increasing individual accountability. Solving the problems is done as a RallyCoach (see the chapter entitled RallyCoach). There is only one paper and one pencil for each pair of students. Person A begins solving a problem in writing and also states aloud what (s)he is doing. Meanwhile, Person B watches and coaches. When done, Person A passes the paper to Person B. If the problem is correct, Person B praises Person A and writes his/her initials next to Person A's work. If the problem is incorrect, Person B coaches and

M I X - P A I R - R A L L Y C O A C H

re-teaches before praising and initialing. Partners now reverse roles, with person B solving a problem and Person A coaching and praising.

Once students have solved the given problems and agree on the answers, there are two ways for them to check their work. One way is to have students hand their papers in to the teacher. Another alternative is to have two pairs join up to create a team of four. Pairs swap papers and offer feedback on each other's work.

Following are several ideas for incorporating Mix-Pair-RallyCoach into the mathematics classroom.

Blackline masters for some of these activities are also included. In some of the activities, the cards are divided into "A cards" and "B cards," each with different types of information on them. When using these card sets, students are to pair up so there is one "A card" and one "B card" in each pair. If a card set is not divided into "A cards" and "B cards," students may form completely random pairs and then decide for themselves who will be Person A and Person B.

Mix-Pair-RallyCoach Contents

PRE-ALGEBRA

- Activities 341
- Blackline Masters 345

ALGEBRA 1

- Activities 351
- Blackline Masters 355

GEOMETRY

- Activities 361
- Blackline Masters 363

ALGEBRA 2

- Activities 369
- Blackline Masters 375

TRIGONOMETRY

- Activities 369

PRE-CALCULUS

- Activities 381
- Blackline Masters 387

Mix-Pair-RallyCoach

Management Tips

1 Before mixing, students should clear everything off their desks except one paper (worksheet) and one pencil for every pair. Once students mix and pair up, they will be sitting down in a new location to work. They will be greeted by a clean work surface and the materials they need.

2 If a Mix-N-Match card set is divided into "A cards" and "B cards," use a different color card stock for each.

4 Students put a hand up as they mix to find a partner; hands go down when a partner is found.

5 You may want to do a "Mix-Pair-Share" as a classbuilder before pairing students for the RallyCoach activity.

Social Skills

1 Coaching others

2 Patience (giving others time to work)

3 Asking for help

4 Appropriate noise level

5 Offering help

6 Giving and accepting praise

7 Giving and accepting constructive criticism

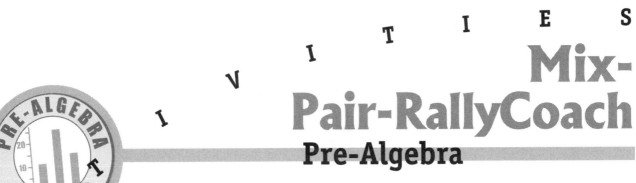

1. OPERATIONS ON FRACTIONS

All the cards handed out have a fraction written on them. Students form random pairs. Person A determines a common denominator for the fractions. Person B the determines the sum or difference of the fractions, according to the teacher's discretion. Another option is to have Person A compute the product of the fractions and Person B compute the quotient.

$$\frac{7}{3}$$

$$\frac{1}{8}$$

2. OPERATIONS ON INTEGERS

Same as "Operations on Fractions," only now the cards handed out each contain an integer instead of a fraction.

-15

+9

3. OPERATIONS ON DECIMALS

Same as "**Operations on Fractions**," only now the cards handed out each contain a decimal instead of a fraction.

.37	1.6

4. PASSAGE OF TIME

On each card is written a certain time of day, such as "3:15 p.m." or "5:12 a.m." Students form random pairs and decide who will be Person A and who will be Person B. Person A determines how much time has elapsed starting with Person A's time and ending with Person B's time. Person B determines how much time would elapse if you started with time B, and ended at time A. Answers should be expressed in hours and minutes, such as "5 hours and 12 minutes."

4:17 pm	9:30 am

5. PERCENT OF A NUMBER

On each card is a whole number. Students form random pairs and decide who will be Person A and who will be Person B. Person A answers the question, "A is what percent of B?" Person B answers the question, "B is what percent of A?"

18	24

6. PERCENT DECREASE (AND PERCENT INCREASE)

Half the cards handed out are "A cards," each of which contains a percent, such as "50%" or "35%." The other cards are "B cards," each of which contains a dollar figure, such as "$5.32" or "$108.50." Students pair up so that there is one "A card" and one "B card" in each pair. Person A determines the dollar discount if the given price is reduced by the given percent. Person B then determines the selling price after the discount. This activity can be modified to include percent increase instead of percent decrease.

A.	B.
75%	$1.16

7. SURFACE AREA AND VOLUME OF PRISMS

Half the cards handed out are "A cards" which describe the shape and dimensions of the base of a prism. For example, "The base is a rectangle with length 13 cm and width 5 cm." or "The base is a circle with a radius of 4 cm." The "B cards" indicate the height of the prism. For example, "The height of the prism is 10 cm." Students pair up so that there is one "A card" and one "B card" in each pair. Person A draws a diagram of the prism. Person B computes the area of the base. Person A then determines the total surface area of the prism. Finally, Person B determines the volume of the prism.

A.	B.
The base is square with sides of 4 cm	The height is 8 cm

pgs. 347-350

8. GREATEST COMMON FACTOR AND LEAST COMMON MULTIPLE

On each card is a whole number. Students form random pairs and decide who will be Person A and who will be Person B. Person A determines the GCF of the two given whole numbers, then Person B determines the LCM of the two numbers.

36

27

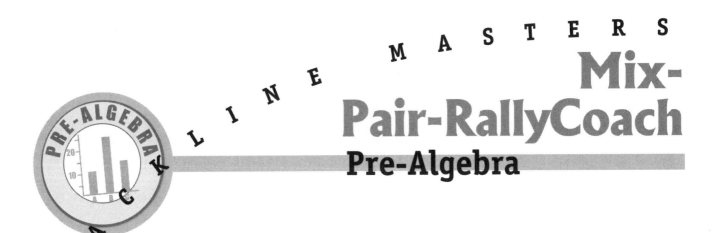

Surface Area and Volume

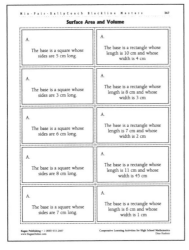

OBJECTIVES

Students will determine the volume and surface area of a prism.

MATERIALS

"Mix-Pair-RallyCoach" cards (see following pages), pencils, RallyCoach worksheet (see following pages)

DIRECTIONS

Half the cards are "A cards" and the other half are "B cards." The "A cards" describe the base of a prism and the "B cards" state the height of the prism. Students find a partner so that each pair contains one "A card" and one "B card." Partners then solve the following problems and record their answers on the RallyCoach worksheet:

Person A draws the prism formed by the base and

height indicated on the cards.

Person B determines the area of the base (to the nearest 100th if necessary).

Person A determines the total surface area of the prism (to the nearest 100th if necessary).

Person B determines the volume of the prism (to the nearest 100th if necessary).

EXTENSION

Once students are comfortable solving the problems above, they can be asked to find more difficult volumes and surface areas. Instead of working with prisms whose bases are rectangles and circles, the bases of the prisms could be parallelograms, trapezoids, or triangles.

Surface Area and Volume

A.

The base is a square whose sides are 5 cm long.

A.

The base is a rectangle whose length is 10 cm and whose width is 4 cm

A.

The base is a square whose sides are 3 cm long.

A.

The base is a rectangle whose length is 8 cm and whose width is 3 cm

A.

The base is a square whose sides are 6 cm long.

A.

The base is a rectangle whose length is 7 cm and whose width is 2 cm

A.

The base is a square whose sides are 8 cm long.

A.

The base is a rectangle whose length is 11 cm and whose width is 45 cm

A.

The base is a square whose sides are 7 cm long.

A.

The base is a rectangle whose length is 6 cm and whose width is 1 cm

Surface Area and Volume

B.

The height of the
prism is 4 cm

B.

The height of the
prism is 5 cm

B.

The height of the
prism is 1 cm

B.

The height of the
prism is 2 cm

B.

The height of the
prism is 47 cm

B.

The height of the
prism is 8 cm

B.

The height of the
prism is 10 cm

B.

The height of the
prism is 11 cm

B.

The height of the
prism is 2.5 cm

B.

The height of the
prism is 3.5 cm

Surface Area and Volume

A.

The base is a circle with radius of 6 cm

B.

The height of the prism is 6 cm

A.

The base is a circle with radius of 4 cm

B.

The height of the prism is 3 cm

A.

The base is a circle with radius of 5 cm

B.

The height of the prism is 9 cm

A.

The base is a circle with radius of 3 cm

B.

The height of the prism is 8.5 cm

A.

The base is a circle with radius of 2 cm

B.

The height of the prism is 5.5 cm

Kagan Publishing • 1 (800) 933-2667
www.KaganOnline.com

Cooperative Learning Activities for High School Mathematics
Dina Kushnir

Surface Area and Volume

Names: _____   _____

Person A: Draw a diagram of the prism with a base as indicated on Card A and height as indicated on Card B.

Person B check and initial:_____

Person B: Find the area of the base of the prism. Round to the nearest 100th if necessary.

Person A check and initial:_____

Person A: Find the total surface area for the prism. Round to the nearest 100th if necessary.

Person B check and initial:_____

Person B: Find the volume of the prism. Round to the nearest 100th if necessary.

Person A check and initial:_____

1. OPERATIONS ON POLYNOMIALS

Each card handed out contains a polynomial, such as "5x + 7" or "$x^2 - 3x + 1$." Students form random pairs and decide who will be Person A and who will be Person B. Person A determines the sum of the polynomials in simplest form. Person B determines the difference of polynomial A minus polynomial B. Person A then determines polynomial B minus polynomial A. Finally, Person B determines the product of the two polynomials.

$5x - 3$	$x^2 + x + 2$

2. OPERATIONS ON MONOMIALS

Each card handed out contains a monomial, such as "$12x^2y^4$" or "$7x^8y$." Students form random pairs and decide who will be Person A and who will be Person B. Person A determines the product of the two monomials and Person B determines the quotient A/B in lowest terms.

$18x^4y^3$	$9xy^2$

Kagan Publishing • 1 (800) 933-2667
www.KaganOnline.com

Cooperative Learning Activities for High School Mathematics
Dina Kushnir

3. WRITING AND SOLVING LINEAR EQUATIONS

On each card is a verbal phrase such as "five more than twice x" or "one-third of x decreased by 7." Students form random pairs and decide who will be Person A and who will be Person B. Person A writes an algebraic equation where card A represents the left member and card B represents the right member. Person B then solves the equation for x. Finally, Person A checks the solution in the original equation.

pgs. 358-360

7 less than twice x

The product of x and 3

4. SOLVING SYSTEMS OF LINEAR EQUATIONS

Each card contains a linear equation in two variables, such as "5x + 7y = 34" or "y = 3x - 10." Students form random pairs and decide who will be Person A and who will be Person B. Person A solves the system for x and Person B solves for y. Be aware that when systems of equations are formed randomly, the solutions are very likely to be "unfriendly" fractions. Students should be comfortable working with fractions before attempting this activity.

y = 2x + 1

3x - 4y = 9

5. IRRATIONAL NUMBERS

On each card is a radical expression, such as $5\sqrt{8}$ or $3\sqrt{8}$. Students form random pairs and decide who will be Person A and who will be Person B. Person A determines which expression is greater using estimation or a calculator. Person B determines the sum A + B in simplest radical form. Person A then determines the product AB in simplest radical form. Finally, Person B determines the value of $(A - B)^2$ in simplest radical form.

$$5\sqrt{18}$$

$$2\sqrt{8}$$

Cooperative Learning Activities for High School Mathematics
Dina Kushnir

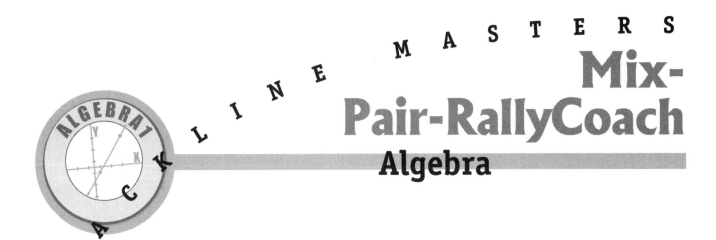

Writing and Solving Linear Equations

OBJECTIVES

Students will translate verbal phrases into algebraic format and solve linear equations.

MATERIALS

"Mix-Pair-RallyCoach" cards (see following pages), pencils, RallyCoach worksheet (see following pages)

DIRECTIONS

Each card contains a verbal phrase, such as "twice x increased by 7." Each students finds a partner and decides who will be Person A and who will be Person B. Partners then solve the following problems and record their answers on the

RallyCoach worksheet:

Person A translates each verbal phrase into algebra and writes the equation formed by setting these two expressions equal to each other.

Person B solves the equation written by Person A. Leave answers in fractional form if necessary.

Once students have finished the above problems, they could trade cards with another pair of students. This time, Person B writes the equation and Person A solves it.

NOTE

During this activity it is possible for students to end up with equations such as the following...

Ex. 1) $2x + 5 = 2(x - 3)$

Ex. 2) $3x - 6 = 3(x-2)$

Equations such as these give the teacher an opportunity to explain that some equations have no solution (like example 1), while others have an infinite number of solutions (like example 2).

Writing & Solving Linear Equations

x increased by 3	seven more than twice x
twice x increased by 1	twice the sum of x and 3
half x increased by 2	the sum of x and 10
two more than x	three times the sum of x and 2
four more than half x	three times x, increased by 7

Writing & Solving Linear Equations

the product of x and 6	x decreased by 5
the product of x and 5, increased by 3	twice x decreased by 9
six more than the product of x and 2	half x decreased by 4
the sum of 3 and twice x	three less than x
the product of x and 3, increased by 10	six less than half x

Writing & Solving Linear Equations

eight less than twice x	the product of x and 9
twice the difference of x and 7	the product of x and 7, decreased by 4
the difference of x and 5	eight less than the product of x and 3
three times the difference of x and 6	twice x decreased by 10
three times x decreased by 2	the product of x and 8, decreased by 1

Cooperative Learning Activities for High School Mathematics
Dina Kushnir

Writing & Solving Linear Equations

Names: _____   _____

Person A: Translate each verbal phrase into algebra. Then write the equation formed by setting these two expressions equal to each other.

Person B check and initial: _____

Person B: Solve the above equation. Leave answer in fractional form if necessary.

Person A check and initial: _____

* Trade cards with another pair of students!!!

Person B: Translate each verbal phrase into algebra. Then write the equation formed by setting these two expressions equal to each other.

Person A check and initial: _____

Person A: Solve the above equation. Leave answer in fractional form if necessary.

Person B check and initial: _____

Kagan Publishing • 1 (800) 933-2667
www.KaganOnline.com

I V I T I E S

Mix-Pair-RallyCoach
Geometry

1. COORDINATE GEOMETRY

Each card handed out contains the coordinates of a point. Students form random pairs and decide who will be Person A and who will be Person B. Person A determines the distance between the two points. Person B determines the midpoint of the line segment connecting the two points. Person A then determines the slope of the line containing the two points. Finally, Person B determines the equation of the line passing through the two points.

pgs. 365-368

(6, -5)

(-8, 0)

2. TRANSFORMATIONAL GEOMETRY

Each card handed out contains the coordinates of a point. Students form random pairs and decide who will be Person A and who will be Person B. Person A determines the rule for the translation so that the image of A is B. Person B determines the point of reflection so that the image of A under this point reflection would be point B.

(0, -7)

(3, 2)

3. MORE TRANSFORMATIONS

Each card handed out contains the coordinates of a point. Students form random pairs and decide who will be Person A and who will be Person B. Person A plots the two points on a piece of graph paper and connects them to form a line segment, $\overline{AB}$. Person B graphs the image of $\overline{AB}$ under a reflection in the x-axis (or y-axis) and labels it $\overline{A'B'}$. Person A then graphs the image of $\overline{A'B'}$ under a reflection in the line y = x and labels it $\overline{A''B''}$. Finally, Person A graphs the image of $\overline{A''B''}$ under a reflection in the origin (or other point given by the teacher) and labels it $\overline{A'''B'''}$. This activity can be extended to include translations, dilations, or rotations.

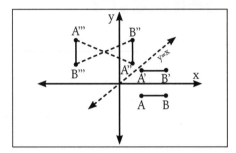

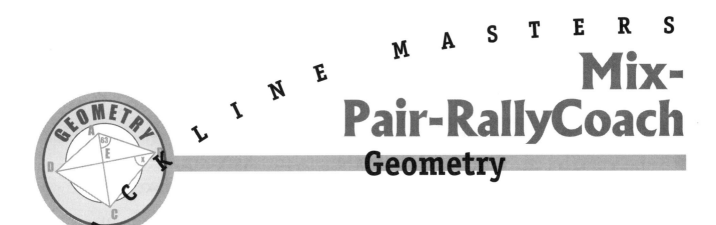

Mix-Pair-RallyCoach
Geometry

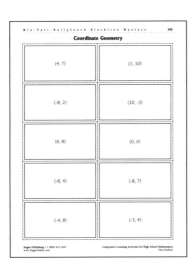

Coordinate Geometry

OBJECTIVES

Students will determine the length, slope, and midpoint of a line segment created by two given endpoints. They will also write the equation of a line passing through two given points.

MATERIALS

"Mix-Pair-RallyCoach" cards (see following pages), pencils, RallyCoach worksheet (see following pages)

DIRECTIONS

On each card is a point, such as (5, 7). The cards are passed out to all students and each student finds a partner. Partners decide who will be Person A and who will be Person B. Partners then solve the following problems and record their answers

Cooperative Learning Activities for High School Mathematics
Dina Kushnir

on the RallyCoach worksheet:

Person A finds, in simplest radical form, the length of the line segment formed by connecting the two points.

Person B determines the midpoint of the line segment formed by connecting the two points.

Person A finds the slope of the line segment formed by connecting the two points.

Person A writes the equation of the line passing through the two points in y = mx + b form.

EXTENSION

Once students are comfortable solving the problems above, try putting students in trios. Students can then do a RoundTable, solving problems such as, "Write the equation of the line that is perpendicular to $\overline{AB}$ and passes through C."

Coordinate Geometry

(4, 7)

(1, 10)

(-8, 2)

(10, -3)

(6, 8)

(0, 0)

(-8, 4)

(-8, 7)

(-4, 8)

(-3, 4)

Coordinate Geometry

(3, -2)	(-9, 2)
(9, -1)	(7, -7)
(-3, 5)	(-5, 7)
(-1, 5)	(8, -7)
(-6, 2)	(-3, -3)

Coordinate Geometry

(0, -2)	(5, -3)
(-4, 4)	(-4, -6)
(0, 1)	(6, -1)
(3, 1)	(9, 3)
(5, 5)	(2, 1)

Coordinate Geometry

Names: _____   _____

Person A: Our two points are _____ and _____. Find the length of the line segment formed by connecting your two points. Express your answer in simplest radical form.

Person B check and initial: _____

Person B: Find the slope of the line segment formed by connecting your two points. Express your answer as a fraction in lowest terms.

Person A check and initial: _____

Person A: State the coordinates of the midpoint of the line segment formed by connecting your two points.

Person B check and initial: _____

Person B: Write the equation of the line passing through your two points. Write your answer in y =mx + b form.

Person A check and initial: _____

Mix-Pair-RallyCoach
Algebra 2 and Trigonometry

1. ABSOLUTE VALUE EQUATIONS AND INEQUALITIES

Half of the cards are "A cards," each containing an absolute value expression, such as $|x - 4|$. The "B cards" contain algebraic expressions which do not involve absolute value, such as "$2x + 1$." Students pair up so that there is one "A card" and one "B card" in each pair. A pairing might look like this...

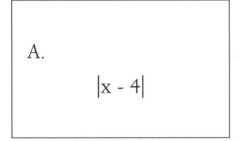

A.	B.
$|x - 4|$	$7x + 5$

Person A would solve the equation $|x - 4| = 7x + 5$. Person B then checks these results and uses them to graph the solution set of $|x - 4| > 7x + 5$ on a number line.

2. COMPOSITIONS OF FUNCTIONS

Half the cards contain an equation for $f(x)$ and half the cards contain an equation for $g(x)$. Students pair up so there is one $f(x)$ and one $g(x)$ in each pair. Person A evaluates $f(g(3))$. Person B evaluates $g(f(-5))$. Person A then writes a rule for $g(f(x))$ in simplest algebraic form. Finally, Person B writes a rule for $f(g(x))$ in simplest algebraic form.

A.	B.
$f(x) = 3x + 7$	$g(x) = x^2 + 1$

3. WRITING THE EQUATION OF A LINE

Half the cards are "A cards," each of which contains the coordinates of a point. The other cards are "B cards," each of which contains the equation of a line. Students pair up so that each pair includes an A and a B. Person A determines the equation of the line parallel to the given line and passing through the given point. Person B determines the equation of the line perpendicular to the given line and passing through the given point.

A. (5, -2)	B. y = 4x -1

4. ANGLE SUM AND ANGLE DIFFERENCE FORMULAS

pgs. 377-380

Half the cards are "A cards" which state a trig function value for $\angle A$. For example, "sinA = $-\dfrac{3}{5}$" or "tan A = $\dfrac{8}{24}$". The "B cards" state a trig function value for $\angle B$. For example, "cosB = $\dfrac{5}{13}$" or "secB = $\dfrac{7}{9}$". Students pair up so there is one A and one B in each pair. Person A determines the value of sin (A + B) in simplest fractional/radical form. Person B then determines the value of tan (A - B) in simplest fractional/radical form. The rally table can continue as long as the teacher sees fit, incorporating any angle sum or angle difference formula.

A. sin A = $\dfrac{4}{7}$	B. sec B = $-\dfrac{11}{5}$

5. GRAPHING SYSTEMS OF INEQUALITIES

Each card contains an inequality in two variables, such as
"$5x^2 + 2y^2 \leq 20$" or "$y \geq x^2 + 5$." Students form random pairs and decide who
will be Person A and who will be Person B. Person A graphs one of the inequalities
on a sheet of graph paper. Person B graphs the other inequality on the same coordinate
plane. Person A then labels the solution set for the system of inequalities formed by the
two cards and states the coordinates of one solution. Finally, Person B checks the
solution named by Person A.

$$x^2 + 4y^2 \leq 36$$

$$y \geq x^2 - 7$$

6. GRAPHING TRIG FUNCTIONS

Half the cards are "A cards" which contain a given value of a, such as "$a = \frac{1}{2}$" or "$a = 4$."
The "B cards" contain a value of b, such as "$b = 3$" or "$b = \frac{1}{4}$." Students pair up so there is
one A and one B in each pair. Person A sketches the graph of $y = a\sin bx$ for $0 \leq x \leq 2\pi$.
Person B sketches the graph of $y = a\cos bx$ for $0 \leq x \leq 2\pi$.

$$a = -2$$

$$b = \frac{1}{2}$$

7. OPERATIONS ON COMPLEX NUMBERS

Each card contains a complex number, such as "5 - 2i" or "3 + 10i." Students form random pairs and decide who will be Person A and who will be Person B. Person A finds the sum of the two complex numbers in a + bi form. Person B finds the difference B - A in a + bi form. Person A then finds the product of the two complex numbers in a + bi form. Finally, Person B finds the quotient $\underline{A}$ in a + bi form.
$$ B$$

7 - 2i

10 + i

8. ADVANCED PROBABILITY COMBINATIONS

Half the cards are "A cards" which indicate how many blue marbles are in a jar, such as "5 blue marbles" or "1 blue marble" The "B cards" state how many red marbles are in the same jar. Students pair up so there is one A and one B in each pair. Person A determines the probability of selecting exactly 2 red marbles and 1 blue marble when 3 marbles are randomly drawn. Person B determines the probability of choosing all the same color marble when 4 marbles are drawn.

A.
There are 6 blue marbles in the jar

B.
There are 3 red marbles in the jar

9. BINOMIAL EXPANSION

Half the cards are "A cards" which contain a binomial, such as (x + 3p) or ($\frac{y}{4}$ - 1). The "B cards" contain an exponent, such as 3 or 4. Students pair up so there is one A and one B in each pair. Person A determines the value of the first term when the given binomial is raised to the given power. Person B finds the value of the third term when the given binomial is raised to the given power.

$$\left(\frac{x}{2} - 3\right)$$

exponent = 4

10. EQUATION OF A CIRCLE

Half of the cards are "A cards" which state the coordinates of the center of a circle. The "B cards" state the radius of the circle. Students pair up so there is one A and one B in each pair. Person A writes the equation of the circle with the given center and radius. Person B writes the equation of a line tangent to the circle and parallel to the x-axis (or y-axis).

A.

center = (5, -1)

B.

radius = 3

Cooperative Learning Activities for High School Mathematics
Dina Kushnir

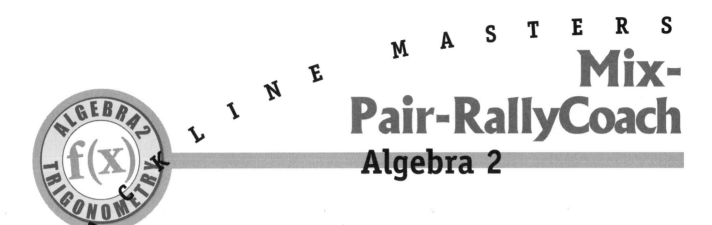

Mix- Pair-RallyCoach
Algebra 2

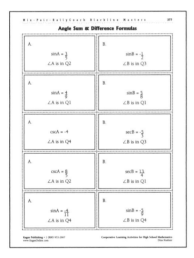

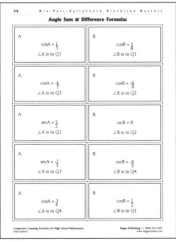

Angle Sum and Difference Formulas

OBJECTIVES

Given one trig function value of Angle A and one trig function value of Angle B, students will determine the value of the sine, cosine and/or tangent of (A + B) or (A - B) in simplest fractional/ radical form

MATERIALS

"Mix-Pair-RallyCoach" cards (see following pages), pencils, RallyCoach worksheet (see following pages)

DIRECTIONS

Half the cards are "A cards" and the other half are "B cards." The "A cards" state a trig function value for Angle A and indicate in which quadrant Angle A is located. The "B cards" state the same information for Angle B. The cards are passed out and the students form pairs so that there is one "A card" and one "B card" in each pair. Partners then solve the following problems and record their answers on the RallyCoach worksheet:

Person A finds the value of $\sin(A + B)$ in simplest fractional/radical form.

Person B finds the value of $\tan(A + B)$ rounded to four decimal places.

Person A finds the value of $\cos(A - B)$ in simplest fractional/radical form.

Person B finds the value of $\sin(B - A)$ in simplest fractional/radical form.

Angle Sum & Difference Formulas

A.

$$\sin A = \frac{3}{5}$$

$\angle A$ is in Q2

B.

$$\sin B = \frac{-1}{2}$$

$\angle B$ is in Q3

A.

$$\sin A = \frac{4}{9}$$

$\angle A$ is in Q1

B.

$$\sin B = \frac{5}{8}$$

$\angle B$ is in Q1

A.

$$\csc A = -4$$

$\angle A$ is in Q4

B.

$$\sec B = \frac{-5}{3}$$

$\angle B$ is in Q3

A.

$$\csc A = \frac{8}{5}$$

$\angle A$ is in Q2

B.

$$\sec B = \frac{13}{4}$$

$\angle B$ is in Q1

A.

$$\sin A = \frac{-4}{11}$$

$\angle A$ is in Q4

B.

$$\sin B = \frac{-5}{9}$$

$\angle B$ is in Q4

Angle Sum & Difference Formulas

A.

$$\cos A = \frac{1}{3}$$
$\angle A$ is in Q1

B.

$$\cos B = \frac{5}{8}$$
$\angle B$ is in Q1

A.

$$\cos A = \frac{-4}{7}$$
$\angle A$ is in Q3

B.

$$\cos B = \frac{-8}{9}$$
$\angle B$ is in Q2

A.

$$\sec A = \frac{5}{2}$$
$\angle A$ is in Q1

B.

$$\csc B = 8$$
$\angle B$ is in Q2

A.

$$\sec A = \frac{-7}{3}$$
$\angle A$ is in Q3

B.

$$\csc B = \frac{-9}{5}$$
$\angle B$ is in Q4

A.

$$\cos A = \frac{3}{4}$$
$\angle A$ is in Q4

B.

$$\cos B = \frac{1}{2}$$
$\angle B$ is in Q1

Angle Sum & Difference Formulas

A.

$$\tan A = \frac{12}{7}$$
∠A is in Q3

B.

$$\tan B = \frac{7}{4}$$
∠B is in Q3

A.

$$\tan A = \frac{-6}{5}$$
∠A is in Q4

B.

$$\tan B = \frac{-10}{9}$$
∠B is in Q4

A.

$$\cot A = -3$$

∠A is in Q2

B.

$$\cot B = \frac{15}{8}$$
∠B is in Q1

A.

$$\cot A = -3$$

∠A is in Q2

B.

$$\cot B = \frac{-11}{5}$$
∠B is in Q2

A.

$$\tan A = \frac{3}{8}$$
∠A is in Q1

B.

$$\tan B = \frac{1}{2}$$
∠B is in Q3

Angle Sum & Difference Formulas

Names: _____   _____

Person A: Find $\sin(A + B)$ in simplest fractional/radical form.

Person B check and initial: _____

Person B: Find $\tan(A + B)$ as a decimal rounded to four places.

Person A check and initial: _____

Person A: Find $\cos(A - B)$ in simplest fractional/radical form.

Person B check and initial: _____

Person B: Find $\sin(B - A)$ in simplest fractional/radical form.

Person A check and initial: _____

*Paper clip your cards to this sheet before handing it in.

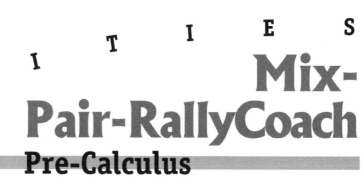

1. Determinants

Each card contains a linear equation in two variables, such as "3x + 4y = 8." Students form random pairs and decide who will be Person A and who will be Person B. Person A finds the value of the determinant D. Person B finds the value of the determinant D_x. Then Person A finds the value of the determinant D_y. Finally, Person B finds the value of x and y using these determinants.

2x -4y = 10

y = 4x -1

2. Arithmetic Series and Sequences

Each card contains a given element in a series. For example, "The 6th term is 12" or "The 12th term is 90." Students form random pairs, and decide who will be Person A and Person B. Students are told that the numbers they have on their cards are terms in an arithmetic progression. Person A must first find d, the common difference. Person B must then determine the value of the first term in the series.

$a_{10} = 5$

$a_3 = -17$

Cooperative Learning Activities for High School Mathematics
Dina Kushnir

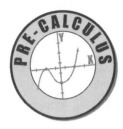

3. GEOMETRIC SERIES

Half the cards are "A cards" which state a given value for a_1, the first term in a geometric progression. The "B cards" state a given value of r, the common ratio. Students pair up so there is one A and one B in each pair. Person A uses the information on the cards to determine the value of the 10th term. Person B finds the sum of the infinite geometric series starting with a_1 and with a common ratio of r.

A.	B.
$a_1 = \dfrac{5}{2}$	$r = \dfrac{1}{2}$

4. PARABOLAS

pgs. 389-392

Half the cards are "A cards" which indicate the coordinates of the vertex of a parabola. The "B cards" contain the equation of a directrix. Students pair up so there is one A and one B in each pair. Person A writes the equation of the parabola with the given vertex and directrix. Person B then finds the coordinates of the focus of the parabola.

A.	B.
vertex (-3, 1)	directrix : y = 5

5. RATIONAL FUNCTION GRAPHS

Half of the cards are "A cards" which contain a polynomial p(x) in factored form, such as "p(x) = 2(x + 3)²(x - 1)." The "B cards" contain a polynomial q(x) in factored form. Students pair up so there is one A and one B in each pair. They put their polynomials together to form the rational function $y = \frac{p(x)}{q(x)}$. The goal of the activity is to sketch the graph of this rational function. Person A determines the equation(s) of the vertical asymptotes. Person B determines the x-intercepts and y-intercept. Person A then writes the equation of the horizontal or diagonal asymptote. Finally, Person B sketches the graph of $y = \frac{p(x)}{q(x)}$.

A.	B.
$p(x) = 3(x + 1)^2 (x - 3)$	$q(x) = (x - 2)^2 (x + 3)$

6. DISTANCE FROM A POINT TO A LINE

Half of the cards are "A cards" which state the coordinates of a point. The "B cards" state the equation of a line in y = mx + b form. Students pair up so there is one A and one B in each pair. Person A rewrites the given line in Ax +By +C = 0 form, where A, B, and C are integers. Person B then finds the distance from the given point to the given line in simplest radical form.

A.	B.
(-7, 3)	$y = \dfrac{2}{3}\, x + 1$

Kagan Publishing • 1 (800) 933-2667
www.KaganOnline.com

Cooperative Learning Activities for High School Mathematics
Dina Kushnir

7. LINEAR FUNCTIONS

On each card is a given function value for f(x), such as "f(5) = 4" or "f(- 3) = 1."
Students pair up so there is one A and one B in each pair. Person A writes a linear
function for f(x) which satisfies the conditions on the two cards. Person B then
writes a formula for f⁻¹ (x).

$f(2) = 3$	$f(-3) = 1$

8. SOLVING EXPONENTIAL EQUATIONS USING LOGS

Each card handed out contains an exponential expression, where the variable x is in
the exponent. For example, 5^{x+2} or 32^x. Students form random pairs and create an
equation by setting their two exponential expression equal to each other. Person A
takes the log of both sides and applies all necessary laws of logarithms. Person B picks
up where Person A left off and solves for x to the nearest hundredth. Finally, Person A
checks the solution in the original equation.

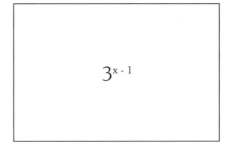

4^{3x}	3^{x-1}

9. VECTORS

On each card is a vector, such as **<**-3,2**>** or **<**4,-8**>**. Students form random pairs, and decide who will be Person A and Person B. Person A determines the cosine of the angle between the two vectors (using the formula $\cos\theta = \frac{A \cdot B}{|A| \cdot |B|}$). Person B then finds the angle between the two vectors to two decimal places, both in degrees and radians.

<**5, -3**>

<**-1, 6**>

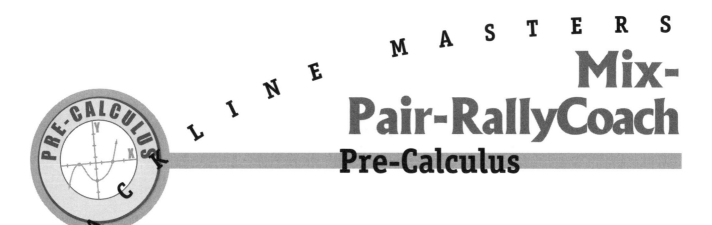

Parabolas

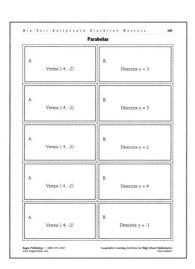

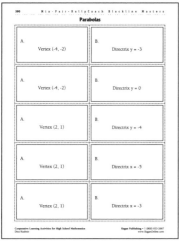

OBJECTIVES

Given the vertex and directrix of a parabola, students will write the equation of the parabola and then state the coordinates of the focus.

MATERIALS

"Mix-Pair-RallyCoach" cards (see following pages), pencils, RallyCoach sheets (see following pages)

DIRECTIONS

Half the cards are "A cards" which state the coordinates of a point. The other cards are "B cards" which state the equation of a line. Cards are handed out and students pair up so there is one "A card" and "B card" in each pair. Students then solve the following problems and record their answers on the RallyCoach worksheet:

Person A writes the equation of a parabola whose vertex is the given point and whose directrix is the given line.

Person B determines the coordinates of the focus of the aforementioned parabola.

Person A writes the equation of the axis of symmetry of the parabola.

Person B determines the focal width of the parabola.

Parabolas

A.	B.
Vertex (-4, -2)	Directrix y = 3
A.	B.
Vertex (-4, -2)	Directrix y = 5
A.	B.
Vertex (-4, -2)	Directrix y = 2
A.	B.
Vertex (-4, -2)	Directrix y = 4
A.	B.
Vertex (-4, -2)	Directrix y = -1

Kagan Publishing • 1 (800) 933-2667
www.KaganOnline.com

Cooperative Learning Activities for High School Mathematics
Dina Kushnir

Parabolas

A. Vertex (-4, -2)	B. Directrix y = -3
A. Vertex (-4, -2)	B. Directrix y = 0
A. Vertex (2, 1)	B. Directrix y = -4
A. Vertex (2, 1)	B. Directrix x = -5
A. Vertex (2, 1)	B. Directrix x = -3

Parabolas

A.

Vertex (2, 1)

B.

Directrix x = -2

A.

Vertex (2, 1)

B.

Directrix x = 0

A.

Vertex (2, 1)

B.

Directrix x = -1

A.

Vertex (2, 1)

B.

Directrix x = 1

A.

Vertex (2, 1)

B.

Directrix x = 3

Kagan Publishing • 1 (800) 933-2667
www.KaganOnline.com

Cooperative Learning Activities for High School Mathematics
Dina Kushnir

Parabolas

Names: _____   _____

Vertex: _____   Directrix: _____

Person A: Write the equation of the parabola whose vertex is the given point and whose directrix is the given line.

Person B check and initial: _____

Person B: State the coordinates of the focus of this parabola. Leave answer in radical form if necessary.

Person A check and initial: _____

Person A: Write the equation of the axis of symmetry for this parabola.

Person B check and initial: _____

Person B: State the focal width of this parabola.

Person A check and initial: _____

STRUCTURES for Mathematics

Fan-N-Pick 1

Find Someone Who 2

Mix-Freeze-Group 3

Numbered Heads Together 4

Pairs Check 5

Showdown 6

Telephone 7

Timed Pair Square 8

Kagan Publishing • 1 (800) 933-2667
www.KaganOnline.com

Cooperative Learning Activities for High School Mathematics
Dina Kushnir

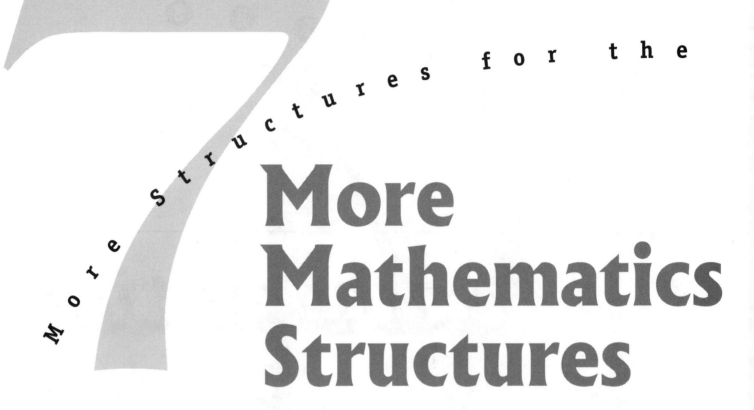

More Mathematics Structures

7 More Structures for the

In this chapter, you will find several other structures that are effective for producing mastery of mathematical content and skills. Depending on the content, some of these structures can also be used for teambuilding, classbuilding, and development of higher level thinking skills. The structures included in this chapter are listed in alphabetical order, and the steps for each of these structures are described in detail.

M a t h e m a t i c s   C l a s s r o o m

More Mathematics Structures

FAN-N-PICK. *396*

FIND SOMEONE WHO *397*
• *Blackline* *398*

MIX-FREEZE-GROUP. *399*

NUMBERED HEADS TOGETHER *400*

PAIRS CHECK *401*

SHOWDOWN *402*

TELEPHONE. *403*
• *Activity* *404*

TIMED PAIR SHARE *405*

Fan-N-Pick

This structure is great for review. The teacher prepares for this structure by making a set of question cards related to classroom content. Students sit in teams of four and number off.

Steps

1 Student One holds the question cards (fans) and says, "Pick a card!"

2 Person Two picks a card, reads the question out loud, and allows some think time.

3 Person Three answers the question.

4 Students four responds to the answer:

• For questions which have right or wrong answers, Student Four checks and then either praises or coaches.

• For higher-level thinking questions which have no right or wrong answer, Student Four praises and paraphrases the thinking that went into the answer.

5 Students rotate roles one clockwise for each new round.

Find Someone Who

This structure can be used for mastery or classbuilding, depending on the types of questions you use. The teacher prepares for this structure by giving each student a sheet of questions or problems. For classbuilding, you might ask questions such as, "Find someone who has visited at least 10 different states." Mastery questions would be directly related to classroom content. For example, "Find someone who can express $(x + 3)(x - 2)$ as a trinomial." A blackline master for a "Find Someone Who" worksheet is on the next page.

Steps

1 Students mix throughout the classroom, keeping a hand up until they find a partner who is not a teammate.

2 In pairs, Person A asks a question from the worksheet and Person B responds. Person A records B's answer on his/her own worksheet.

3 Person B checks and initials the answer.

4 Person B asks a question from the worksheet and Person A responds. Person B records the answer on his/her worksheet.

5 Person A checks and initials the answer.

6 Partners shake hands, part, and raise a hand again in search of a new partner.

7 Students repeat steps 1 – 6 until their worksheets are complete.

8 When their worksheets are completed, students sit down; others can approach seated students as a resource.

9 In teams, students compare answers. If there is any disagreement or uncertainty they raise four hands to ask a team question.

Cooperative Learning Activities for High School Mathematics
Dina Kushnir

Find Someone Who...

My Name

Mix-Freeze-Group

This structure is used for mastery but also acts as a classbuilder. The teacher prepares a set of questions to which the answer is a number or a multiple choice with a corresponding numerical key. (See the examples below.)

Steps

1 Students mix around the room.

2 Teacher calls, "Freeze."

3 Students freeze.

4 Teacher poses a question, which can be stated orally or put on an overhead. The question has a numeric answer or the answer is a multiple choice with a numeric key. Some examples are shown below.

Example:
Solve the equation $3x + 1 = 13$ (numerical answer)

Example:
The graph shown is an example of what type of function?

2. Logarithmic
3. Exponential
4. Linear,
5. Quadratic, 6. Trigonometric
(multiple choice with a numeric key)

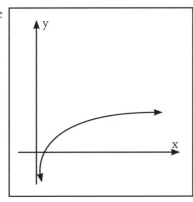

5 Students group according to the number and kneel down. (i.e. – if the answer is "3," you kneel in a group of three people.)

6 Students not in a group go to the "Lost and Found" at the front of the room.

7 Students stand and teacher poses a new question. The class must be sure that the same students cannot be left over for the Lost and Found twice in a row.

Optional: Once students know the game, students in the Lost and Found may be the ones to generate and ask the next question. After they ask a question, they rush to form a group.

Numbered Heads Together

This structure can be used for mastery or developing higher-level thinking skills, depending on the types of questions posed by the teacher. The students work in teams during this structure.

Steps

1 Students number off.

2 The teacher poses a problem and gives think time.

Examples:

*Express (tanA)(cscA) in terms of a single trigonometric function.

*What do all of these graphs have in common?

*Write the equation or graph of a function whose domain is…

3 Students lift up from their chairs ("Bottoms Up!") to put their heads together, discuss, and teach.

4 Students sit down when everyone knows the answer or has something to share.

5 The teacher calls a number. The student with that number from each team stands.

6 The standing students share their answers simultaneously using…

*Slate Share   *Choral Response

*Finger Response   *Chalkboard Response

*Response Cards   *Manipulatives

7 Teammates praise the student who responded for the team.

Management Tip: This structure can get tricky if not all teams are comprised of four students. What do you do if you call for student #4 to stand and a team has only three members? The solution is a Student Selector spinner, shown at left. It automatically selects one student from each team, even if you have different sized teams working at once. The random nature of spinning assures that students are always on their toes, since they never know who will be called on next! Available from Kagan.

Pairs Check

In this structure, students sit in teams of four, one pair of students on each side of the table ("shoulder partners"). The teacher prepares a worksheet with questions and problems on it. There is only one paper and one pencil per pair.

Steps

1 In teams, shoulder partners are formed. Person A in each pair does the first problem, both in writing and talking aloud. Person B watches, coaches, and praises.

2 Partners reverse roles. Person B does the second problem while Person A watches, coaches, and praises.

3 Pairs check with their other teammates ("face partners") after every two problems. Papers go to the middle of the table for comparison. Teammates coach and correct if needed.

4 The team celebrates after reaching agreement on the two problems.

5 Shoulder partners repeat steps 1 and 2, doing two more problems. Pairs continue to check with their face partners after every two problems.

Showdown

This structure is great for review of classroom content and skills. To prepare, the teacher writes review problems on cards (only one problem per card).

Steps

1 Question cards are stacked in the center of the team table.

2 The teacher selects one student on each team to be the Showdown Captain for the first round. The Showdown Captain draws the top card and reads the question aloud.

3 Working alone, all students write their answers in notebooks or on slates.

4 When finished, teammates signal they are ready with a "thumbs up."

5 The Showdown Captain calls, "Showdown!"

6 Teammates show their answers and the Showdown Captain leads the checking.

7 If everyone agrees on the correct answer, the team celebrates. If not, the teammates coach and then celebrate.

8 The person on the left of the Showdown Captain becomes the new Showdown Captain for the next round. Repeat from step 2.

Telephone

In this structure, students teach their teammates new information.

Steps

1 One person from each team ("The Learner") is selected to leave the room.

2 The remaining students ("The Teachers") receive instruction.

3 The Teachers plan how to best instruct the Learner and who will teach each part. Each team member takes a part of the teaching. (Use the blackline master on the next page. Give one to each "Teacher.")

4 The learners return to their teams.

5 The Teachers each teach their part of the content in turn. Teammates augment if necessary.

6 The learners take a practice test or do a check – out activity.

Management Tip: Make arrangements with a nearby teacher pal to take in the Learners when they are sent out of the room.

Telephone
My Notes

Divided the labor. Who will teach what part?

_____
name

_____
part

_____
name

_____
part

_____
name

_____
part

_____
name

_____
part

Timed Pair Share

This structure is used for answering higher level thinking questions (no right or wrong answer) or sharing information. Students work with partners.

Steps

1 The teacher announces a topic or poses a question. The teacher states how long each student will have to share.

Examples:

*What do you already know about…?

*What are some practical applications of…?

*What were you thinking when…?

*How does _____ affect _____?

*What would happen if…?

2 Teacher provides think time.

3 In pairs, Person A shares for the allotted time while Person B listens.

4 Person B responds and paraphrases. (Examples: "I liked what you said about…" "One thing I learned from you was…")

5 Pairs switch roles. Person B shares while Person A listens.

6 Person A responds.